CONTENTS

i

1–8 The G...
a taste of things t... ...

9–24 Lifestyles, Singles, Couples – all ages
teenagers to the over sixties; people at home and at play; loving, relaxing, spending time and spending money, eating and drinking, enjoying life; their friendships, worries and concerns ...
for many more, see 25–64, Health & Beauty 127–133, and Vacations 134–144

25–26 Christmas, Weddings, Celebrations

27–44 Families, Children, Babies
children and parents at home and at play; three generation families; pregnancy, babycare, growing up, relationships ...

45–46 Education and Social Issues
teaching and training, key issues of today ...

47–64 Fitness, Sports – leisure and professional
a mix of leisure and professional sports from athletics to yachting; the excitement of sport at top level, and more lifestyles ...

65–85 Business
success and failure, teamwork, decision making, meetings, training and office life; hard work and stress; people on the move, in the office and at home; multinational businesses, small businesses ...

86–87 Finance
stock exchanges, commodities, currencies, bullion and bonds ...

88 Crowds, Consumers, Disasters, Insurance Themes

89–100 Industry, Technology, Research
research and development, hi-tech, telecommunications, production lines and control rooms, heavy and light industries ...

101–102 Architecture, Construction
domestic, commercial and industrial ...

103–108 Transport – land, sea and air
roads and highways, planes, trains, cars, motor bikes, trucks, shipping and freight ...

109–116 Ideas
symbols, metaphors expressing teamwork, harmony, balance, challenge, success ...

117–120 World, Maps, Space
new ways and old to show the world and its continents, satellite views, major trading blocs and countries; the earth in space ...

121–126 Healthcare, Medicine
caring for the patient, hi-tech facilities, emergency services; surgeons, doctors, nurses and therapists; injury and disease ...

127–133 Health & Beauty – male and female
style and good looks, nutrition and healthy living, beautiful skin, healthy hair and supple bodies ...

134–144 Vacations, Leisure, Sun
lifestyles in the sun; adults and children of all ages on vacation, on the beach ...

145 Tropical Islands and Beaches
...way from it all, palm fringed beaches, ...onely islands, sparkling water ...

146–195 World travel
business and tourist destinations, people of the world; magnificent scenics ...

196–213 Backgrounds and Scenics
backgrounds for text, for composite images; textures and product settings, moons and stars, fireworks, seas and skies, storms and lightning; generic scenics: deserts, mountains and volcanoes, polar regions ...

214–218 Environment – positive and negative images
recycling, alternative energy, flourishing forests and landscapes ... pollution, endangered species, deforestation, congestion ...

219–223 Agriculture
farmers and suppliers, crops and domestic animals, planting and harvesting, vineyards ...

224–225 Food and Flowers

226–235 Wildlife
from African to amphibian, in their natural habitats; and some pets ...

236–240 The James Balog Portfolio
exploring the relationship between humans and chimpanzees

YOUR TEAM AT TONY STONE IMAGES

All your needs will be looked after by your Tony Stone Images team – your personal account executive, picture researcher and team assistant. They want to learn about you and your company, and to help with your particular requirements. Whenever you call you'll speak to the same team, ensuring that picture selections are relevant to your needs and that any special servicing or pricing arrangements are always observed.

MORE IMAGES – WIDER SELECTIONS

Remember, we have thousands of other images which we can't possibly include in this catalogue. So if you can't find the subject or situation you're looking for, or need a broader selection, call us to describe exactly what you need. We'll work with you to help you find just the right shot. To help us help you, please give us as much information as you can, or better still send us a rough layout or sketch by fax. That way, you can be sure you won't be disappointed.

DEADLINES AND DELIVERY

We'll make sure you have the right transparencies on your desk at the right time. Just let us know what *your* deadline is – and we'll make sure we keep to *our* deadline. A same-day service is available to most UK clients.

OUR SERVICE CHARGE

Where appropriate, picture research and standard delivery costs are covered by our non-refundable service charge.

OUR PRICING AND LICENSING POLICY

When you want a price to reproduce any image please give us all the details of the intended usage and we'll be happy to quote a competitive fee. Once you've confirmed which images you plan to use, we'll send you our invoice and licence, subject to the desired reproduction rights being available (see below).

RIGHTS CONTROL

When you need our images for any major use, our rights control service will give you that extra peace of mind. It is designed to protect you or your client from any prominent usage of the same or similar images by your competitors.

COPYRIGHT

All images in this catalogue are the copyright of Tony Stone Images or our *contributing photographers.*

QUALITY DUPES – QUALITY PRINTING

We invite you to compare the print quality of this catalogue with any other stock photography catalogue. It is a showcase of our images, but also shows you the capabilities of our transparencies in print. All of the images were printed from enlarged and enhanced dupes, created in-house by our own colour technicians, though variances in colour to the transparency can occur during the repro/print process. We have also cropped the majority of images for layout purposes. *The dupes we send you are identical to the ones used on this catalogue,* which means that the repro house and printer you work with can also achieve similar quality (please bear in mind that the expertise of the repro houses and printers you choose, inks and paper can also influence the final result). If you have any concerns please feel free to call your personal account executive.

IMAGING TECHNOLOGY

At Tony Stone Images we are committed to significant investment in the latest imaging technology. Our in-house Electronic Imaging System enables us to clean up any blemishes or imperfections, ensuring the transparencies we produce for you are both colour-correct and technically flawless. Additionally, our experienced workstation operators create exciting new images and enhance the work produced by our photographers, as part of our commitment to building the finest file of stock imagery available.

CD-ROM CATALOGUES

For the last two years we have been developing CD-ROM technology. Later this year we will offer you a substantial collection of our images on CD-ROM. If you would like us to keep you informed of future developments, please fill out one of the reply-paid cards at the back of this catalogue.

MORE CATALOGUES

Don't miss out on our previous catalogues – make sure you have a full set of volumes 10, 11 and 12. If you or your colleagues need more, please call us or send one of the reply paid cards at the back of this catalogue.

A MESSAGE FROM TONY STONE

It was just 18 years ago that I produced my first catalogue of stock photography: a modest 8-page affair packed with images in sharp focus, rather formally posed in bright colours. I believe it was among the very first stock catalogues to be issued anywhere in the world, and for its day it was a good professional job.

Times have changed. Dozens of stock catalogues are issued every year. Stock itself has changed radically, and we at Tony Stone Images continue to work to ensure that the images we offer you achieve the quality of the finest commissioned work. And I would like to pay a tribute here to the outstanding photographers from around the world whose work we are proud to present to you in this catalogue.

A word about style in our latest photography. Our research tells us you are interested in natural, candid images with a sense of realism; new and innovative methods in photography, including, frankly, some experimental photographic techniques; and, importantly, an ever-widening range of subjects, locations and ideas.

This is what we have tried to do in this latest catalogue. And since none of this can mean very much to you unless it is backed by friendly and efficient service, we have made Quality Service our watchword for the year.

Finally, I believe we have a duty to our customers to be at the forefront of the technological revolution in our industry, including the digital storage, manipulation and transmission of images. Our company is devoting major human and financial resources to this area, the better to serve your needs through the nineties and beyond.

I hope you find these pages both pleasurable and practical.

T

IE I   Aaron Jones

Jurgen Reisch

TONY STONE
IMAGES

3E 1   Chronis Jons

THE GALLERY

4E 1   Carol Ford

5E 1   Bruce Ayres

6E 1   David Madison

8E 1   Alastair Laidlaw

10E 1 Bruce Ayres

10E 2 Peter Correz

10E 3 Peter Correz

10E 4 Dan Bosler

10E 5 Dale Durfee

10E 6 Carol Ford

10E 7 Peter Correz

10E 8 Ken Fisher

11E 1 Jurgen Reisch

11E 3 Peter Correz

11E 2 Dan Bosler

11E 4 John Running

11E 5 John Running

12E 1 André Perlstein

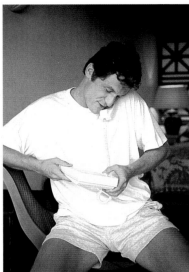

12E 2 André Perlstein

12E 3 Peter Correz

12E 4 Dan Bosler

12E 5 Oli Tennent

12E 6 Penny Tweedie

12E 7 Lee Page

12E 8 Peter Correz

12E 9 Ken Fisher

13E 1 Peter Correz

13E 2 Frank Orel

13E 3 Dan Bosler

13E 4 Bruce Ayres

13E 5 Dale Durfee

13E 6 Gary Nolton

13E 7 Bruce Ayres

14E 1 David Leach

14E 2 Bruce Ayres

14E 3 Dan Bosler

14E 4 Chris Harvey

14E 5 Frank Herholdt

14E 6 Andrew Sacks

14E 7 Dan Bosler

15E 1 Frank Orel

15E 2 Lee Page

15E 3 Ken Fisher

16E 1 Peter Correz

16E 2 André Perlstein

16E 3 Chris Harvey

16E 4 André Perlstein

16E 6 James Darell

16E 5 Dale Durfee

16E 7 Dale Durfee

16E 8 David Madison

16E 9 Peter Correz

17E 1 Peter Correz

17E 2 Bruce Ayres

17E 3 Gerard Loucel

17E 4 André Perlstein

17E 5 Peter Correz

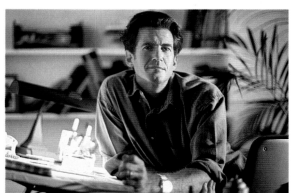

17E 6 Dan Bosler

17E 8 Chad Slattery

17E 7 Ken Fisher

18E 2 Bruce Ayres

18E 1 Peter Correz

18E 3 Bob Torrez

18E 4 Peter Correz

18E 6 Bruce Ayres

18E 5 Peter Correz

18E 7 Peter Correz

18E 8 Paul Rees

18E 9 Ken Fisher

19E 1 Scott Robinson

19E 2 André Perlstein

19E 3 Bruce Ayres

19E 5 Dan Bosler

19E 4 Ken Fisher

19E 8 Lori Adamski Peek

19E 7 Dan Ham

19E 6 Tony Latham

20E 2 Christopher Bissell

20E 1 James Darell

20E 3 Penny Tweedie

20E 4 Lee Page

20E 6 Christopher Bissell

20E 5 Chris Harvey

20E 7 Dale Durfee

20E 8 Oli Tennent

20E 9 Ken Fisher

21E 1 Dale Durfee

21E 2 Bruce Ayres

21E 3 Bruce Ayres

21E 5 Ken Fisher

21E 4 Frank Orel

22E 1 Christopher Bissell

22E 2 Chris Harvey

22E 3 Dan Bosler

22E 4 Tony Latham

22E 5 Ken Fisher

22E 6 Robert Shafer

22E 7 Penny Tweedie

22E 8 André Perlstein

22E 9 Peter Correz

23E 1 Dan Bosler

23E 2 Dale Durfee

23E 3 Dale Durfee

23E 4 Bruce Ayres

23E 7 André Perlstein

23E 5 John Waterman

23E 6 Dan Bosler

23E 9 Ralf Schultheiss

23E 8 Peter Correz

24E 3 Christopher Bissell

24E 2 Christopher Bissell

24E 4 Peter Correz

24E 1 Jamey Stillings

24E 5 Bruce Ayres

24E 6 Tony Latham

24E 7 Tony Latham

24E 8 Penny Tweedie

24E 9 Tony Latham

24E 10 Tony Latham

25E 1 Peter Correz

25E 4 Peter Correz

25E 2 Dale Durfee

25E 3 Dale Durfee

25E 7 Dale Durfee

25E 5 Paul Dance

25E 6 Christopher Bissell

26E 1 Dale Durfee

26E 2 Dale Durfee

26E 3 Dale Durfee

26E 6 Dale Durfee

26E 4 Aaron Jones, Aaron Jones Studios

26E 5 Rosemary Weller

26E 7 Ian O'Leary

26E 8 Rick Rusing

26E 9 David Joel

26E 10 Peter Cade

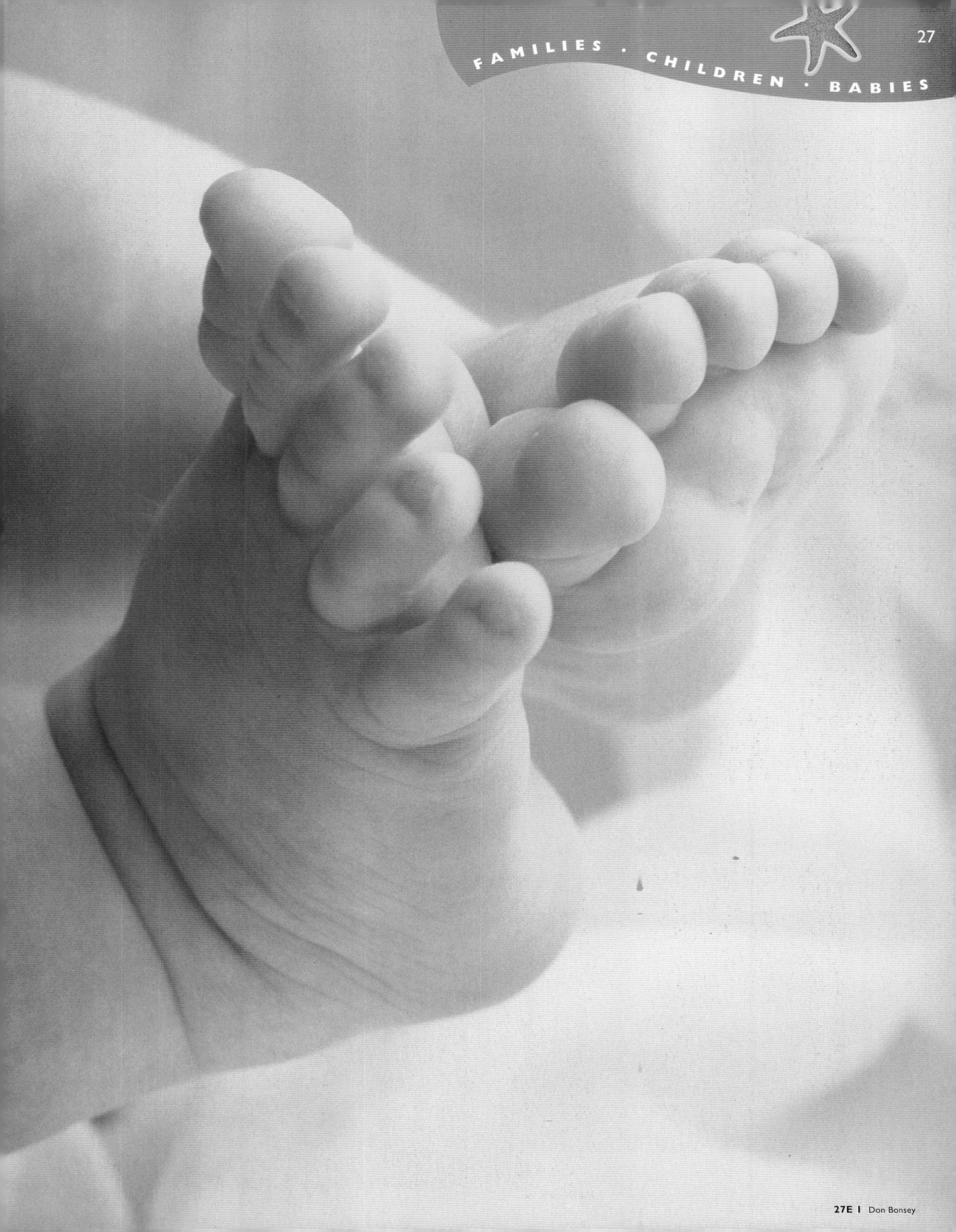

27E | Don Bonsey

28E 1 Arthur Tilley

28E 2 Peter Correz

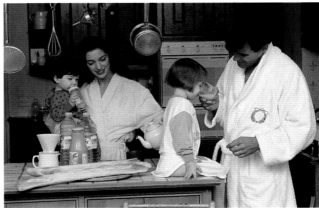

28E 3 James Darell

28E 4 Don Smetzer

28E 5 Andrew Sacks

28E 6 Howard Grey

28E 7 Gerard Loucel

28E 8 Dan Bosler

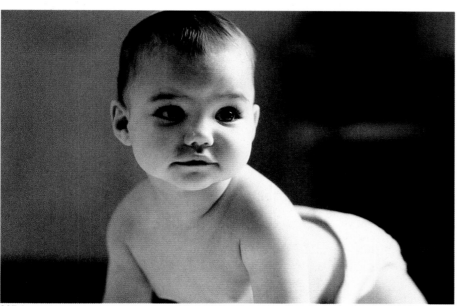

29E 1 Dale Durfee

29E 3 Dale Durfee

29E 2 Bruce Ayres

29E 4 Bob Thomas

29E 5 Jamey Stillings

30E 1 Lori Adamski Peek

30E 2 Arthur Tilley

30E 3 Dale Durfee

30E 4 Dale Durfee

30E 5 Bruce Ayres

30E 6 Peter Correz

30E 7 Jamey Stillings

30E 8 Dan Bosler

31E 1 David Hanover

31E 2 Peter Correz

31E 3 Gerry Soifer

32E 1 Sue Ann Miller

32E 2 Peter Cade

32E 3 Lori Adamski Peek

32E 4 Peter Correz

32E 5 Martin Rogers

32E 6 Andrew Sacks

32E 7 Peter Correz

32E 8 Pascal Crapet

32E 9 Peter Correz

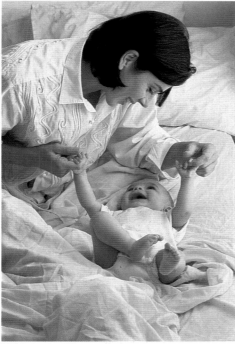

33E 1 Sue Ann Miller

33E 2 Joe Cornish

33E 3 Andrew Sacks

33E 4 Andrew Sacks

33E 5 Charles Thatcher

33E 6 Dan Bosler

33E 7 Bruce Ayres

34E 1 Bruce Ayres

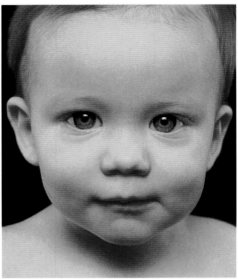

34E 2 Penny Gentieu

34E 3 Philip & Karen Smith

34E 4 Peter Correz

34E 5 Mark Lewis

34E 6 Howard Grey

34E 7 Joe Cornish

34E 8 Peter Correz

35E 1 Charles Thatcher

35E 3 David Hanover

35E 2 Penny Gentieu

35E 4 Dan Bosler

35E 5 Phil Borges

36E 1 Dan Bosler

36E 2 David Hanover

36E 3 Peter Correz

36E 4 Penny Gentieu

36E 5 Dale Durfee

36E 6 Dan Bosler

36E 7 Dale Durfee

36E 8 Andrew Sacks

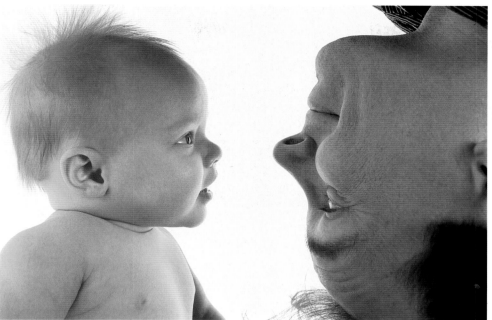

37E 1 Penny Gentieu

37E 2 Peter Correz

37E 3 Martin Rogers

38E 2 Penny Gentieu

38E 1 Dale Durfee

38E 5 Arthur Tilley

38E 3 Dale Durfee

38E 4 Peter Correz

38E 8 Peter Correz

38E 6 Dale Durfee

38E 7 Ian Shaw

38E 9 Jo Browne & Mick Smee

39E 1 Sally Mayman

39E 2 Bruce Ayres

39E 3 Charles Thatcher

39E 4 Peter Cade

39E 7 Carol Ford

39E 5 Peter Correz

39E 6 Claudia Kunin

40E 2 Peter Poulides

40E 1 Sue Ann Miller

40E 3 Frank Orel

40E 4 Penny Gentieu

40E 5 Penny Gentieu

40E 6 Peter Correz

40E 7 Peter Correz

40E 8 Dale Durfee

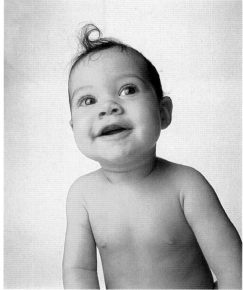

41E 1 Penny Gentieu

41E 2 Howard Grey

41E 3 Dale Durfee

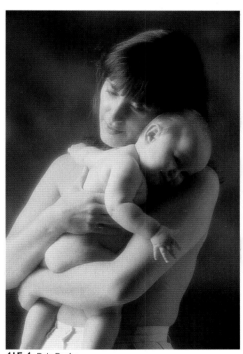

41E 4 Dale Durfee

41E 5 Ken Fisher

41E 6 Lori Adamski Peek

41E 7 Nicole Katano

42E 1 Penny Gentieu

42E 2 Penny Gentieu

42E 3 Frank Orel

42E 4 Claudia Kunin

42E 6 Frank Herholdt

42E 7 Peter Correz

42E 5 John Fortunato

42E 8 Bob Thomas

42E 9 Peter Correz

43E 1 Dale Durfee

43E 2 Dennis O'Clair

43E 3 Peter Correz

43E 4 Dennis O'Clair

43E 5 Dale Durfee

43E 6 Peter Correz

43E 7 Bruce Ayres

44E 1 Dale Durfee

44E 2 Peter Cade

44E 3 Andrew Sacks

44E 4 Peter Correz

44E 5 Lori Adamski Peek

44E 6 Nicole Katano

44E 7 Peter Correz

44E 8 Chris Harvey

44E 9 Chris Harvey

44E 10 Peter Correz

45E 1 Bob Krist

45E 2 Andrew Sacks

45E 5 Bob Krist

45E 3 Pascal Crapet

45E 4 David Joel

45E 6 Bob Krist

45E 7 Andrew Sacks

45E 8 Terry Vine

45E 9 Bob Krist

45E 10 Chip Henderson

46E 3 David Hanover

46E 1 Jurgen Reisch

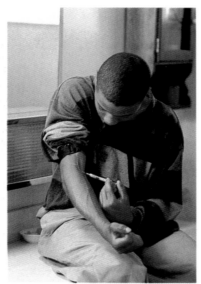

46E 2 David Young-Wolff

46E 4 Matthew McVay

46E 5 Bruce Ayres

46E 6 Jamey Stillings

46E 7 Tony Latham

46E 8 Jurgen Reisch

46E 9 Tony Latham

46E 10 Penny Tweedie

48E 1 Bruce Ayres

48E 2 Tony Henshaw

48E 3 Carol Ford

48E 4 Lori Adamski Peek

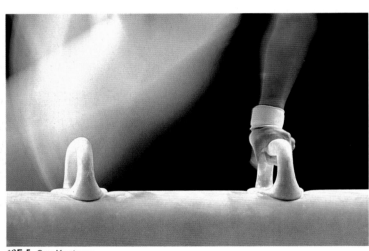

48E 5 Gray Mortimore

48E 6 Dan Bosler

48E 9 Lori Adamski Peek

48E 7 David Madison

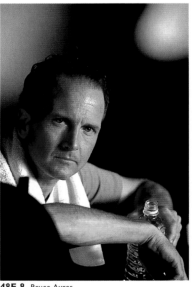

48E 8 Bruce Ayres

49E 1 Carol Ford

49E 2 David Madison

49E 3 Carol Ford

49E 4 Lori Adamski Peek

49E 5 David Madison

49E 6 Bill Staley

49E 7 David Madison

50E 1 Lester Lefkowitz

50E 2 Lori Adamski Peek

50E 3 Lori Adamski Peek

50E 4 Dennis O'Clair

50E 5 Dennis O'Clair

50E 6 Dennis O'Clair

50E 7 Lori Adamski Peek

50E 8 Lori Adamski Peek

51E 1 Sean Arbabi

51E 2 Gray Mortimore

51E 3 Bob Thomas

51E 4 Bob Thomason

51E 5 Bruce Ayres

51E 6 Dennis O'Clair

51E 7 David Madison

51E 8 Lori Adamski Peek

52E 1 Bruce Ayres

52E 2 David Madison

52E 3 Lori Adamski Peek

52E 4 David Madison

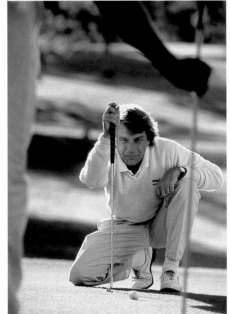

52E 5 Bruce Ayres

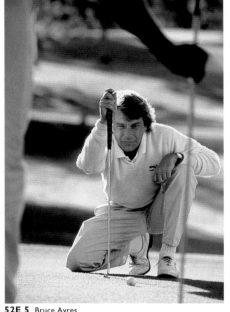

52E 6 David Madison

52E 8 Lori Adamski Peek

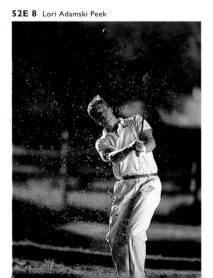

52E 7 Lori Adamski Peek

52E 9 Lori Adamski Peek

53E 1 Dave Cannon

53E 2 Jo McBride

53E 3 Bruce Ayres

54E 1 David Madison

54E 2 Lori Adamski Peek

54E 3 Bob Torrez

54E 4 Bruce Ayres

54E 5 David Madison

54E 6 Bruce Ayres

54E 7 David Madison

54E 8 Dave Cannon

54E 9 David Madison

55E 1 Brian Bailey

55E 2 Jo McBride

55E 3 Jeanne Drake

55E 6 David Madison

55E 4 Richard Elliott

55E 5 John Chard

55E 7 Hugh Sitton

55E 8 Jo McBride

56E 1 Karl Weatherly

56E 2 Lori Adamski Peek

56E 3 Karl Weatherly

56E 4 Jean-François Causse

56E 5 Mike Powell

56E 6 David Madison

56E 7 David Madison

56E 8 Brian Atkinson

57E 1 David Madison

57E 2 David Madison

57E 3 Darrell Wong

57E 4 Warren Bolster

57E 5 Simon Bruty

57E 6 Darryl Torckler

57E 7 Dugald Bremner

57E 8 Karl Weatherly

58E 1 Jo McBride

58E 2 David Madison

58E 3 Glyn Kirk

58E 4 Darrell Wong

58E 5 David Madison

58E 6 Darrell Wong

58E 7 Mike Timo

58E 8 Oli Tennent

59E 1 Mark Junak

59E 2 Bob Torrez

59E 3 Jess Stock

59E 4 Dennis O'Clair

59E 5 Jess Stock

59E 6 Jess Stock

59E 8 Bob Torrez

59E 9 Jess Stock

59E 7 David Madison

60E 1 Lori Adamski Peek

60E 2 Karl Weatherly

60E 3 Jess Stock

60E 4 Jean-François Causse

60E 6 Mark Junak

60E 5 Jess Stock

60E 7 Jess Stock

60E 8 Jess Stock

60E 9 Jean-François Causse

61E 1 Jess Stock

61E 2 Lori Adamski Peek

61E 3 Jess Stock

61E 4 Shaun Botterill

61E 5 Lori Adamski Peek

61E 6 Lori Adamski Peek

61E 7 Bob Torrez

61E 8 Jess Stock

61E 9 David Madison

62E 1 Bob Thomas

62E 2 Dave Cannon

62E 3 Ian Murphy

62E 4 Dan Smith

62E 5 Bob Thomas

62E 6 David Madison

62E 7 David Madison

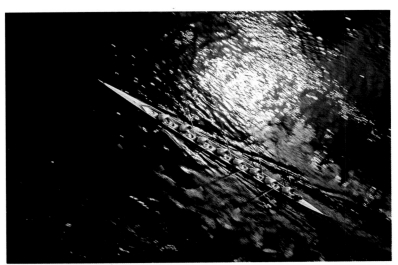

62E 8 David Madison

63E 1 Bob Thomas

63E 2 David Madison

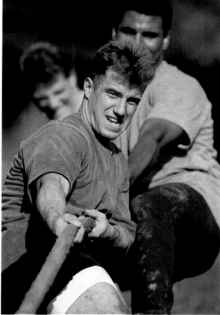

63E 3 David Madison

63E 4 David Madison

63E 5 David Madison

63E 6 Bob Thomas

63E 7 Bob Thomas

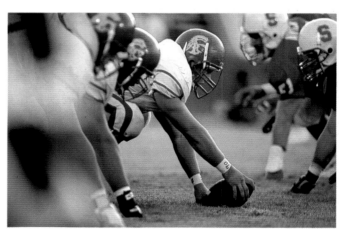

63E 8 David Madison

64E 2 Jan Kopec

64E 3 Jean-François Causse

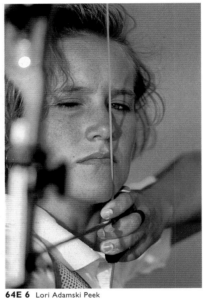

64E 1 Alexander Hubrich

64E 4 Chris Cole

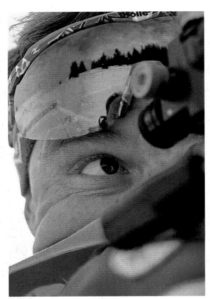

64E 5 Nathan Bilow

64E 6 Lori Adamski Peek

64E 7 Chris Cole

64E 8 Dennis O'Clair

64E 10 Thomas Zimmermann

64E 9 Glyn Kirk

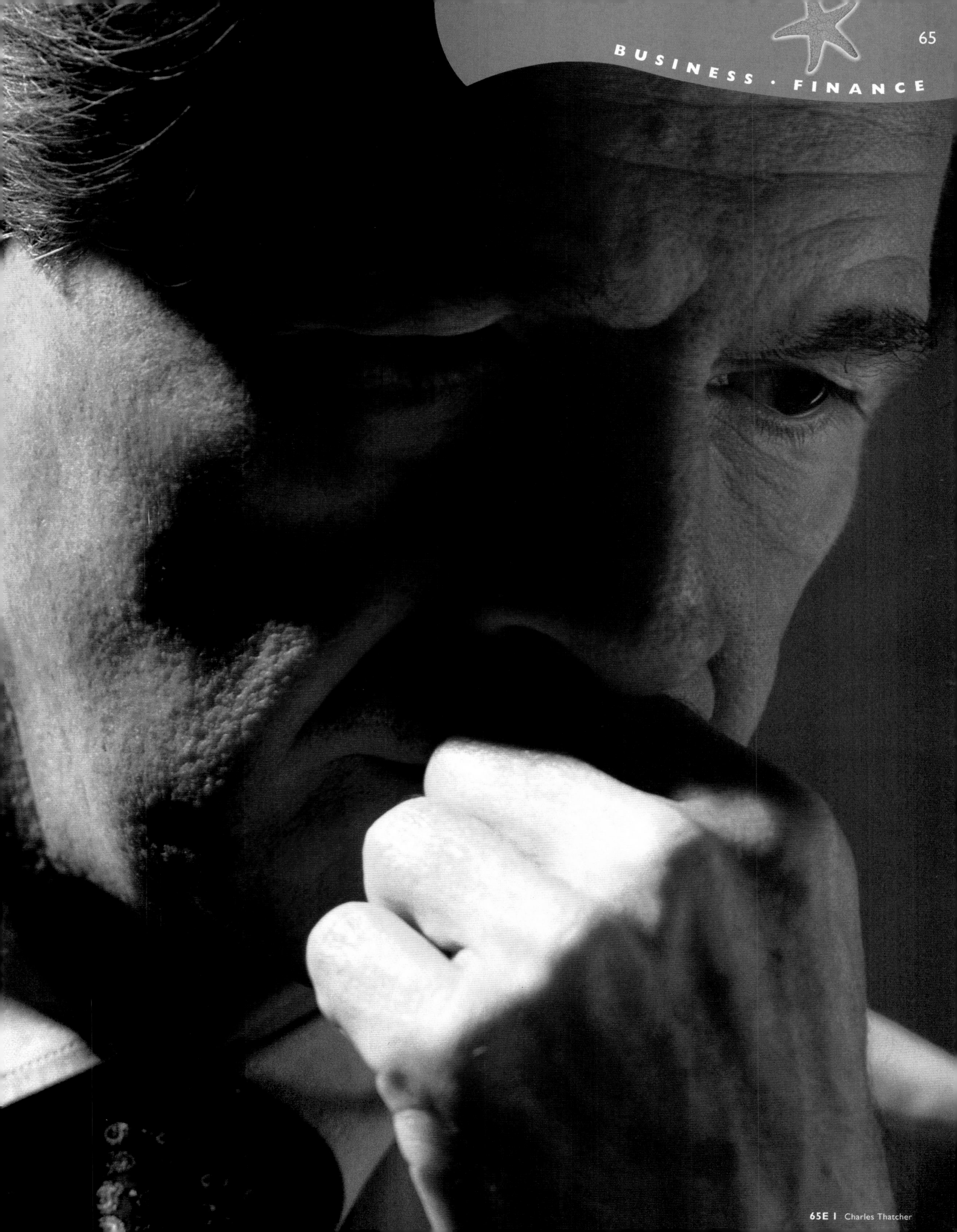

65E I Charles Thatcher

66E 1 Frank Herholdt

66E 2 David Ash

66E 3 Tim Brown

66E 4 Bruce Ayres

66E 5 David Ash

66E 6 Charles Thatcher

66E 7 Frank Herholdt

67E 1 Peter Correz

67E 2 Bruce Ayres

67E 3 Charles Thatcher

67E 4 Scott Robinson

67E 5 Charles Thatcher

68E 1 Howard Grey

68E 2 Charles Thatcher

68E 3 Donovan Reese

68E 4 Terry Vine

68E 5 Tim Brown

68E 6 Frank Herholdt

68E 7 Frank Herholdt

68E 8 Terry Vine

68E 9 Neil Farrin

69E 1 Bruce Ayres

69E 2 Bruce Ayres

69E 3 Charles Thatcher

70E 1 Bruce Ayres

70E 2 David Ash

70E 3 Lonnie Duka

70E 4 Joseph Pobereskin

70E 5 Charles Thatcher

70E 6 Neil Selkirk

70E 7 Frank Herholdt

70E 8 Tim Brown

71E 1 Mark Harris

71E 2 Jeff Zaruba

71E 3 David Hanover

71E 4 Bruce Ayres

71E 5 Mark Lewis

71E 6 Bruce Ayres

71E 7 Frank Herholdt

© TONY STONE IMAGES 1994

72E 1 Charles Thatcher

72E 2 Mark Segal

72E 3 Frank Herholdt

72E 4 Bruce Ayres

72E 5 Stephen Johnson

72E 7 Frank Herholdt

72E 6 Bruce Ayres

72E 8 Tim Brown

73E 1 Andrew Sacks

73E 2 David Ash

73E 3 Terry Vine

73E 4 Herb Schmitz

73E 7 David Ash

73E 5 Howard Grey

73E 6 Frank Herholdt

74E I Bruce Ayres

74E 2 Charles Thatcher

74E 3 Frank Herholdt

74E 4 Howard Grey

74E 5 Frank Herholdt

74E 6 Bruce Ayres

74E 7 Bruce Ayres

74E 8 Bruce Ayres

75E 1 Charles Thatcher

75E 3 Bruce Ayres

75E 2 Frank Herholdt

75E 4 David Ash

75E 5 Bruce Ayres

76E 1 Bruce Ayres

76E 2 Philip Habib

76E 3 Bruce Ayres

76E 4 Tim Brown

76E 5 Joseph Pobereskin

76E 6 Bruce Ayres

76E 7 Frank Herholdt

76E 8 Doug Armand

77E 1 Terry Vine

77E 2 Charles Thatcher

77E 3 Charles Thatcher

77E 4 Bruce Ayres

77E 5 Bruce Ayres

77E 6 Bruce Ayres

77E 7 Bruce Ayres

78E 1 Bruce Ayres

78E 2 Philip Habib

78E 3 Roger Tully

78E 4 Bruce Ayres

78E 5 Frank Herholdt

78E 6 Jon Riley

78E 7 Phil Jason

79E 1 Frank Herholdt

79E 2 Bruce Ayres

79E 3 Frank Herholdt

79E 4 David Tejada

79E 5 Frank Herholdt

79E 6 Bruce Ayres

79E 7 David Ash

80E 1 Dennis McColeman

80E 2 Bruce Ayres

80E 5 Charles Thatcher

80E 3 Charles Thatcher

80E 4 Frank Herholdt

80E 6 Bruce Ayres

80E 7 Bruce Ayres

80E 8 Roger Tully

81E 1 Bruce Ayres

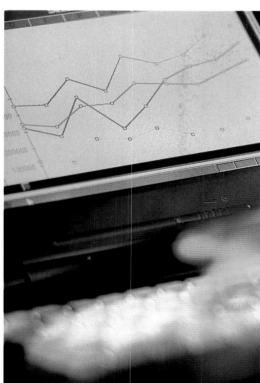

81E 2 Charles Thatcher

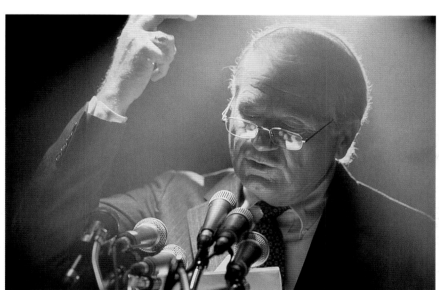

81E 3 Bruce Ayres

81E 4 Bruce Ayres

81E 5 Bruce Ayres

82E 1 Frank Herholdt

82E 2 Lonnie Duka

82E 3 Ralph Mercer

82E 4 Frank Herholdt

82E 5 Bruce Ayres

82E 6 Frank Herholdt

82E 7 Tim Brown

83E 1 Tim Brown

83E 2 Frank Herholdt

83E 3 Lonnie Duka

83E 4 Don Smetzer

83E 5 Howard Grey

83E 6 Frank Herholdt

83E 7 Frank Herholdt

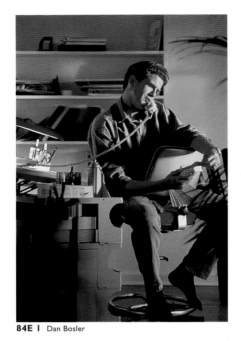

84E 1 Dan Bosler

84E 2 Frank Herholdt

84E 3 Dale Durfee

84E 4 Bruce Ayres

84E 5 Dan Bosler

84E 8 David Ash

84E 6 Frank Herholdt

84E 7 Dan Bosler

85E 1 Dan Bosler

85E 2 Dan Bosler

85E 3 Bob Krist

86E I Frankfurt Stock Exchange/Ed Pritchard

86E 2 Doug Armand

86E 3 Paul Dance

86E 6 Lloyd's of London/Ed Pritchard

86E 4 Martin Rogers

86E 5 Andrew Sacks

86E 9 Ralph Mercer

86E 7 the City, Lloyd's of London/Ed Pritchard

86E 8 (also available as US dollar, French franc, German mark and Japanese yen)/Ed Honowitz

87E 1 Gregg Hadel

87E 2 Jack Vearey

87E 3 Tokyo Stock Exchange/Tim Flach

87E 4 Ralph Mercer

87E 5 Annabelle Breakey

87E 7 Ralph Mercer

87E 6 (also available in US dollars, French francs and German marks)/Phil Jason

87E 8 New York Stock Exchange/Jon Riley

88E 1 Brian Atkinson

88E 2 Jean-Marc Truchet

88E 3 Chris Craymer

88E 4 Chronis Jons

88E 5 Christopher Bissell

88E 6 Ed Pritchard

88E 7 Alan Levenson

88E 8 Stephen Johnson

88E 9 Zigy Kaluzny

88E 10 Arnulf Husmo

88E 11 John Garrett

10 X
N.A..25
∞

90E 1 Terry Vine

90E 2 testing soil for toxicity/Keith Wood

90E 3 technician preparing microscope slide/Howard Grey

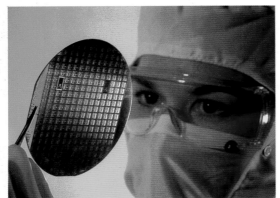

90E 4 silicon wafer/Bruce Ando

90E 5 Lester Lefkowitz

90E 6 Ralph Mercer

90E 7 chemist extracting liquid waste from glass vessel/Keith Wood

90E 8 sewage treatment plant/John Edwards

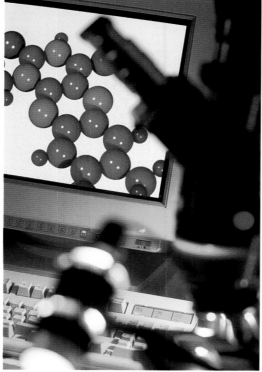

91E 1 computer-generated molecular structure/Chronis Jons

91E 2 computer quality control/Andrew Sacks

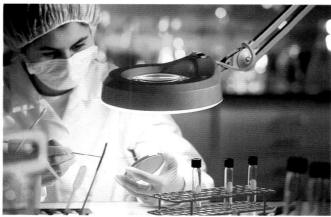

91E 3 preparation of Petri dish cultures/Lonny Kalfus

91E 4 gathering water samples for analysis at chemical plant/Keith Wood

91E 5 Ralph Mercer

91E 6 botanical research, artificial pollination/David Joel

91E 7 behavioural research, Rhesus monkey with surrogate
mother/Martin Rogers

92E 1 testing effect of new drug on living tissue/Terry Vine

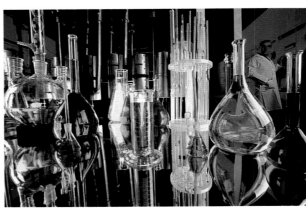

92E 2 testing waste water from power plant/Keith Wood

92E 4 Barry Bomzer

92E 3 telephone exchange/Ron Scott

92E 5 optical fibres/Greg Pease

92E 6 Charles Thatcher

92E 7 Phil Jason

92E 8 measuring atmospheric levels of hazardous waste with Lel meter
Greg Pease

92E 9 hard drive memory discs/Alan Levenson

93E 1 Charles Thatcher

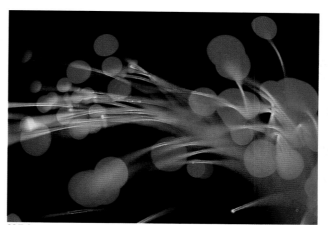

93E 2 optical fibres/Paul Brierley

93E 3 computer-aided design/Dan Bosler

93E 4 silicon wafer in holder/Rich LaSalle

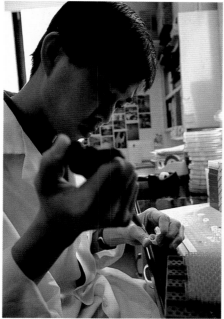

93E 5 biomedical research/David Joel

93E 6 testing water for toxicity/Phil Degginger

93E 7 hazardous waste analysis/Terry Vine

© TONY STONE IMAGES 1994

94E 1 semiconductor production/Rich LaSalle

94E 2 circuit board repair/Andrew Sacks

94E 3 parabolic dish of deep space tracking station
Chad Slattery

94E 4 cheque processing centre/Dennis O'Clair

94E 5 power plant control room/Charles Thatcher

94E 6 radio telescopes/Lester Lefkowitz

94E 8 pharmaceutical production/Barry Bomzer

94E 7 solar power station/Suzanne Geary

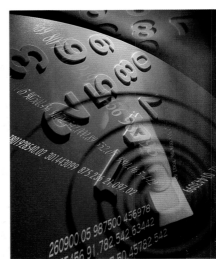

94E 9 Ralph Mercer

95E 1 circuit board assembly line/Andrew Sacks

95E 2 plastic medical products manufacture
David Joel

95E 3 control panel/Martin Rogers

95E 4 quality inspection of pistons/Martin Rogers

95E 5 quality control of video cassette recordings/Dennis O'Clair

95E 6 geothermal power plant control room/Keith Wood

95E 8 paper-mill control room/Greg Pease

95E 9 print separation preparation/David Joel

95E 7 radio telescope/Peter Pearson

96E 1 car engine assembly/Andrew Sacks

96E 2 Mark Segal

96E 3 tractor assembly line, Poland
Zygmunt Nowak-Soliński

96E 6 Andrew Sacks

96E 4 loading freight train/Greg Pease

96E 5 loading timber at dockside/Bruce Hands

96E 7 ship in dry dock/William Helsel

96E 8 John Edwards

96E 9 Andrew Sacks

96E 10 jet engine inspection/Ken Whitmore

97E 1 loading container onto truck/Chronis Jons

97E 2 paint spraying/Andrew Sacks

97E 3 Boeing 757 production/Matthew McVay

97E 4 dockyard, Japan/Chronis Jons

97E 5 Bruce Hands

97E 6 Keith Wood

97E 7 Chris Kapolka

97E 8 Andrew Sacks

97E 9 shipyard workers exercising, Japan/Martin Rogers

98E 1 liquid gas storage tank/Lester Lefkowitz

98E 2 North Sea oil rig/Arnulf Husmo

98E 3 oil rig drill maintenance/Martin Rogers

98E 4 chemical manufacturing plant/Keith Wood

98E 5 geothermal energy plant/Keith Wood

98E 6 oil rig workers/Keith Wood

98E 7 North Sea oil rig/Will Stanley

98E 8 North Sea oil rig/Arnulf Husmo

98E 9 petrochemical plant/Rich LaSalle

98E 10 cement plant control room
Charles Thatcher

99E 1 oil pipeline, Alaska, USA/Ken Whitmore

99E 2 oil rig maintenance/Arnulf Husmo

99E 3 oil storage depot/Martin Rogers

99E 4 oil and gas refinery/Mark Leman

99E 5 petrochemical plant/Keith Wood

99E 6 paint manufacture/Lonnie Duka

99E 7 petrochemical plant/Keith Wood

99E 8 North Sea oil rig construction/Kristian Hilsen

99E 9 oil and gas rig, Pacific/Bob Thomason

100E 2 coal-powered power station/Colin Raw

100E 1 warehouse/John Lund

100E 3 Stephen Studd

100E 4 water feed pipes and cooling tower of power plant/Keith Wood

100E 5 warehouse/David Joel

100E 8 Hoover Dam, Nevada, USA/Peter Lamberti

100E 6 steel foundry/Joseph Sterling

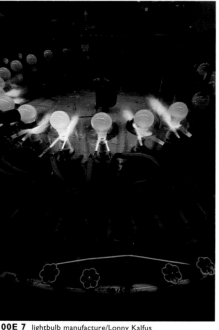

100E 7 lightbulb manufacture/Lonny Kalfus

101E 1 Chronis Jons

101E 2 Charles Thatcher

101E 3 Richard Braine

101E 5 Jon Ortner

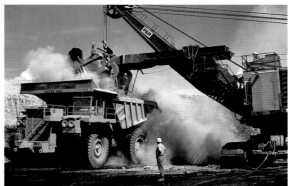

101E 4 opencast coal mine/Lester Lefkowitz

101E 6 steel production/Arnulf Husmo

101E 7 rolls of sheet aluminium/Lonnie Duka

101E 8 Bruce Hands

102E 1 Jon Ortner

102E 2 Donovan Reese

102E 3 Andrew Sacks

102E 4 Charles Thatcher

102E 5 Howard Grey

102E 6 Charles Thatcher

102E 7 Peter Poulides

102E 8 Donovan Reese

102E 9 computer-aided design/Ralph Mercer

102E 10 civil engineering, computer-aided design

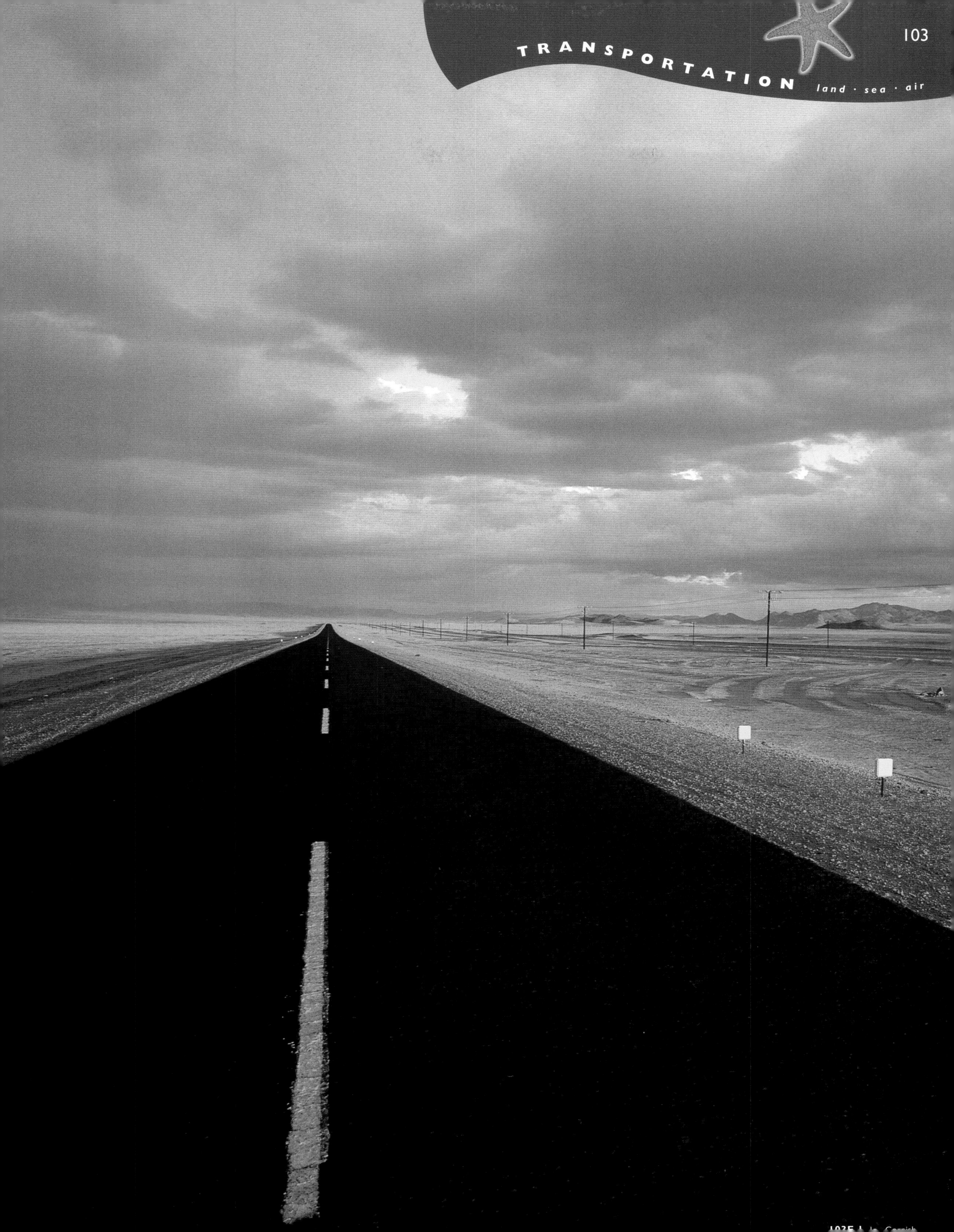

103E Joe Cornish

104E 1 Charles Thatcher

104E 2 Mark Wagner

104E 3 Mark Wagner

104E 4 Peter Poulides

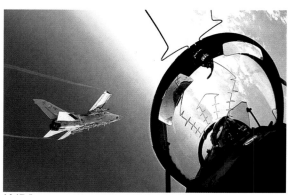

104E 5 fully armed Tornado/Barry Lewis

104E 6 Olaf Soot

104E 7 Austin Brown

104E 8 air traffic control/David Tejada

104E 9 Mark Lewis

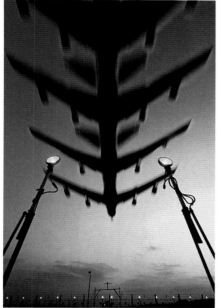

105E 1 Mark Wagner

105E 2 Austin Brown

!05E 3 Peter Poulides

105E 4 Boeing 747 flight-deck/Mike Vines

105E 5 Mark Wagner

105E 7 Mark Wagner

105E 6 Rainer Grosskopf

106E 1 (left-hand drive also available)/Joe Cornish

106E 2 (right-hand drive also available)/Mark Lewis

106E 3 (left-hand drive also available)/Donald Johnston

106E 4 motorway under construction/Pascal Crapet

106E 5 Dennis O'Clair

106E 6 Barry Marsden

106E 7 (left-hand drive also available)/Donald Johnston

106E 8 Rick Rusing

106E 9 Rick Rusing

106E 10 Kristian Hilsen

107E 1 Chris Cheadle

107E 2 Peter Poulides

107E 3 Fred George

107E 4 Donovan Reese

107E 5 (left-hand drive also available)/Dennis O'Clair

107E 6 Nicholas Parfitt

107E 7 Martyn Goddard

108E 1 Oli Tennent

108E 2 David Maisel

108E 3 Martin Rogers

108E 4 John Edwards

108E 5 Jan Kopec

108E 6 Charles Thatcher

108E 7 John Lund

108E 8 Kim Blaxland

108E 9 Don Spiro

108E 10 Martin Rogers

110E 1 Aaron Jones, Aaron Jones Studios

110E 2 Terry Vine

110E 3 Ralph Mercer

110E 4 Stuart McClymont

110E 5 Alastair Laidlaw

110E 6 Pete McArthur

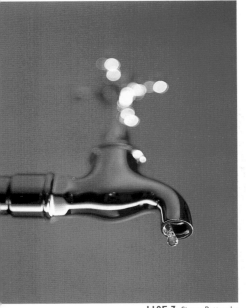

110E 7 Simon Battensby

110E 8 Simon Battensby

110E 9 Douglas Struthers

111E 1 Antonia Deutsch

111E 2 Antonia Deutsch

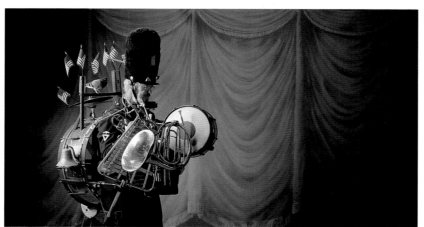

111E 3 Nick Vedros, Vedros & Associates

111E 4 Nick Vedros, Vedros & Associates

111E 6 Stephen Johnson

111E 7 Simon Battensby

111E 5 Ron Berg, Vedros & Associates

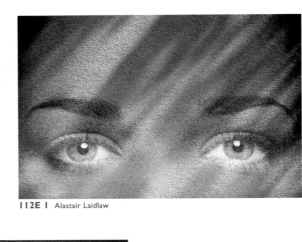
112E 1 Alastair Laidlaw

112E 2 Sean Ellis

112E 3 Pete McArthur

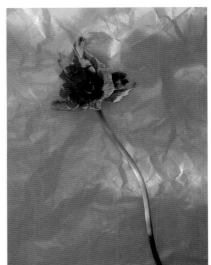
112E 4 Tif Hunter

112E 5 Stuart McClymont

112E 6 Philip Habib

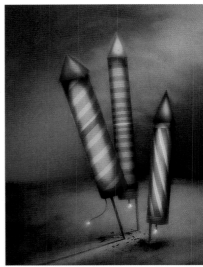
112E 9 Aaron Jones, Aaron Jones Studios

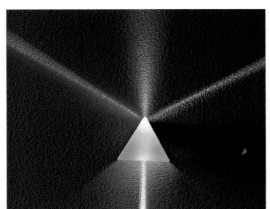
112E 7 Philip Habib

112E 8 Ralph Mercer

113E 1 Stuart McClymont

113E 2 Antonia Deutsch

113E 3 Ray Massey

113E 4 Terry Vine

113E 5 Myron Taplin

113E 6 Ron Berg, Vedros & Associates

113E 7 Robert Bullivant

114E 1 Tim Flach

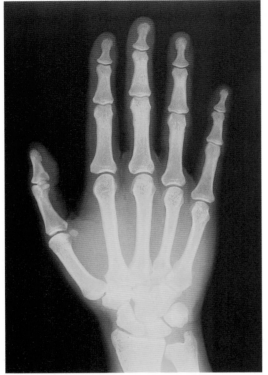
114E 2 RNHRD

114E 3 John Garrett

114E 4 Donovan Reese

114E 5 Mike Powell

114E 6 John Lund

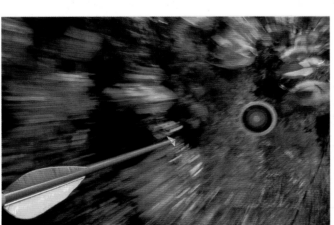
114E 7 Dennis O'Clair

114E 8 John Lund

115E 1 Ralph Mercer

115E 2 Aaron Jones, Aaron Jones Studios

115E 3 Aaron Jones, Aaron Jones Studios

115E 4 Aaron Jones, Aaron Jones Studios

115E 5 Sean Ellis

115E 6 David Ash

115E 7 Ken Whitmore

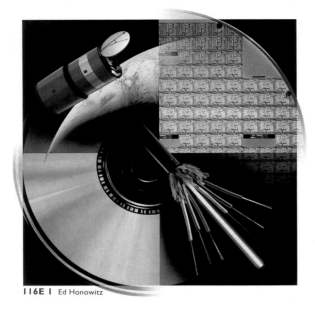

116E 1 Ed Honowitz

116E 2 Philip Habib

116E 3 Simon Battensby

116E 4 Garry Hunter

116E 5 Douglas Struthers

116E 6 Ed Honowitz

116E 7 John Lund

116E 8 John Lund

118E 3 Ralph Mercer

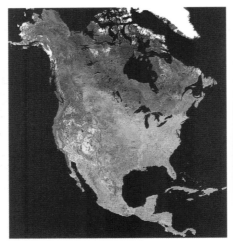
118E 2 North America/Nigel Press

118E 1 Europe (other views available)/Ian O'Leary

118E 6 Americas (Europe also available)/Tim Flach

118E 4

118E 5 Europe (other views available)/Ian O'Leary

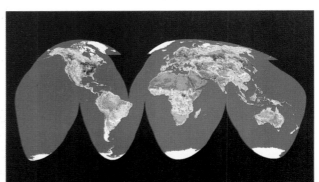
118E 7 Australia and Pacific ocean (other views available)/Ian O'Leary

118E 8 Tim Flach

118E 9 world vegetation/Nigel Press

119E 2 hurricane cloud formation over Europe/IS Ltd

119E 3 Ron Berg, Vedros & Associates

119E 1 Europe (North America also available)
Garry Hunter

119E 4 Aaron Jones, Aaron Jones Studios

119E 5 North America and Europe
TSI, Oxford Cartographers

119E 6 Europe/Ian O'Leary

119E 7 world showing ocean topography/Earth Imaging

119E 8 North America (other views available)
TSI, Oxford Cartographers

119E 9 Ed Honowitz

119E 10 Charles Thatcher

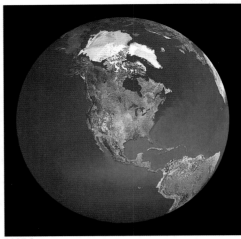

120E 3 North America/Earth Imaging

120E-2 Chris Thomaidis

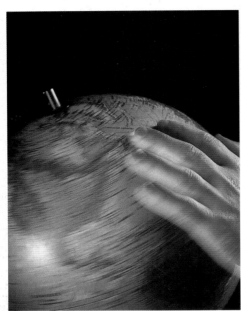

120E 5

120E 1 Charles Thatcher

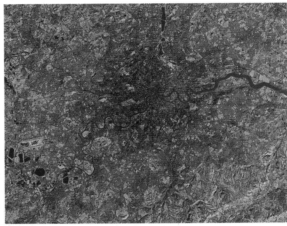

120E 4 London/Nigel Press

120E 6 David Rigg

120E 7 British Isles/Tim Flach

120E 8 Phil Jason

120E 9 Far East and Australia (other views available)
TSI, Oxford Cartographers

120E 10 Eurasia (other views available)
TSI, Oxford Cartographers

122E 1 pharmacy/Bruce Ayres

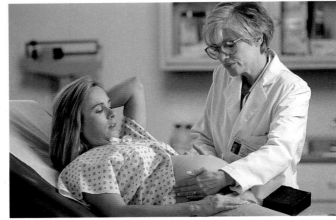

122E 2 Bruce Ayres

122E 3 Peter Poulides

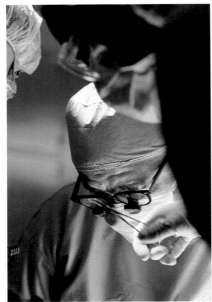

122E 4 Charles Thatcher

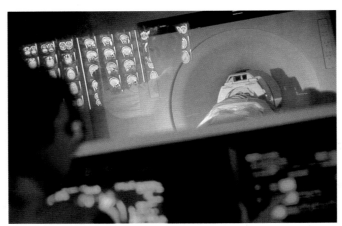

122E 5 MRI control console and scanner/Chronis Jons

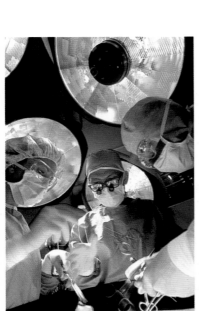

122E 6 Chronis Jons

122E 7 psychotherapy session/Bruce Ayres

122E 8 Andrew Sacks

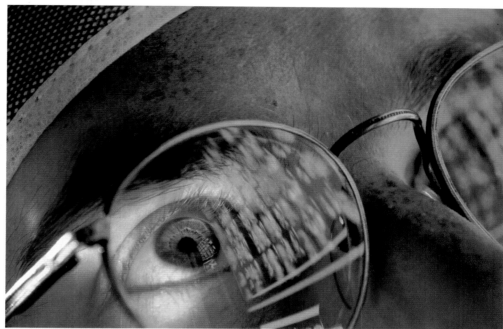
123E 2 doctor inspecting MRI scans/Chronis Jons

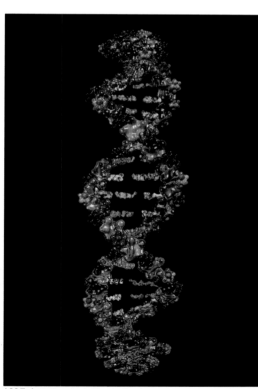
123E 1 condoms/Charles Thatcher

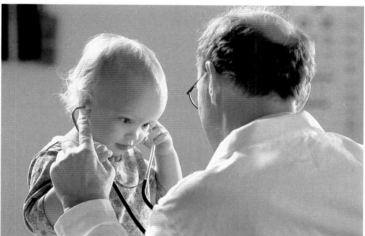
123E 3 Andrew Sacks

123E 4 DNA molecule/Douglas Struthers

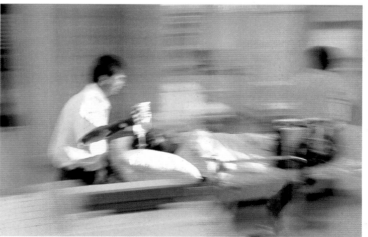
123E 5 casualty/Chronis Jons

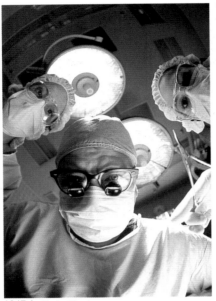

124E 1 Charles Thatcher

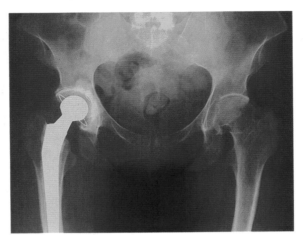

124E 2 pelvis x-ray showing hip replacement/RNHRD

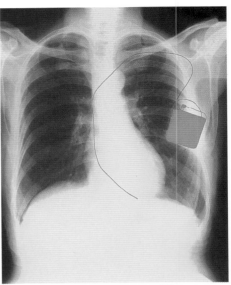

124E 3 chest x-ray showing pacemaker/RNHRD

124E 4 Tom Raymond

124E 5 Zigy Kaluzny

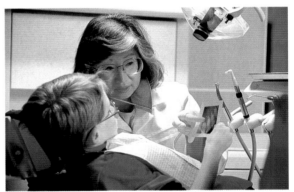

124E 8 dentist explaining treatment to child/Andrew Sacks

124E 6 psychotherapy session/Zigy Kaluzny

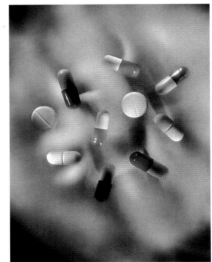

124E 7 Paul Dance

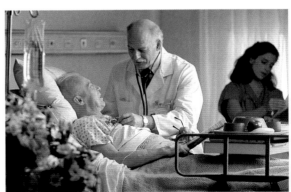

124E 9 Bruce Ayres

125E 1 vitamin C/Spike Walker

125E 2 AIDS virus/Douglas Struthers

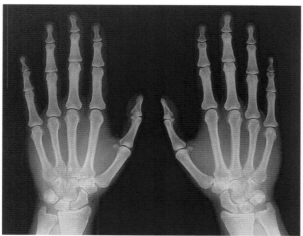

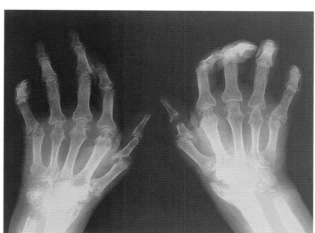

125E 3 x-ray of normal hands/RNHRD

125E 4 x-ray of rheumatoid arthritic hands/RNHRD

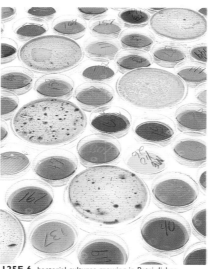

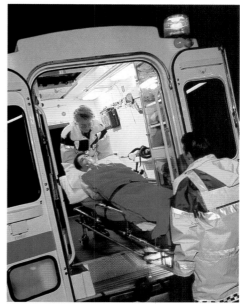

125E 5 cellular analysis using light microscope/Martin Rogers

125E 6 bacterial cultures growing in Petri dishes
Phil Degginger

125E 7 ambulance/Chris Baker

126E 1 Charles Thatcher

126E 2 anaesthetist/Charles Thatcher

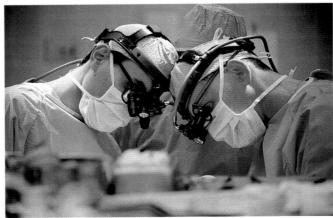

126E 3 Andrew Sacks

126E 4 laboratory refrigerator storing blood samples/Lonny Kalfus

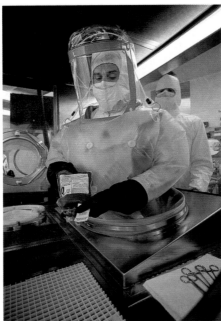

126E 5 blood products research/David Joel

126E 6 family therapy session/Bruce Ayres

126E 7 Bruce Ayres

126E 8 Bruce Ayres

126E 9 physiotherapy/Peter Poulides

128E 1 André Perlstein

128E 2 André Perlstein

128E 3 Carol Ford

128E 5 Peter Correz

128E 6 Carol Ford

128E 4 Ralf Schultheiss

128E 7 James Darell

128E 8 James Darell

128E 9 Chris Harvey

129E 1 Chris Harvey

129E 2 James Darell

129E 3 Carol Ford

129E 4 Chris Harvey

129E 5 André Perlstein

129E 6 James Darell

129E 7 Bruce Ayres

© TONY STONE IMAGES 1994

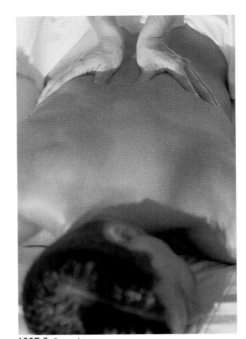

130E 3 Alastair Laidlaw

130E 2 Bruce Ayres

130E 1 Alastair Laidlaw

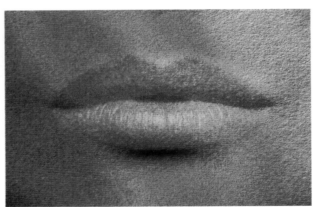

130E 4 Alastair Laidlaw

130E 5 James Darell

130E 6 Tim Flach

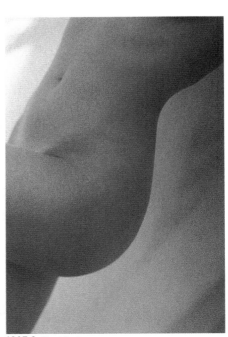

130E 7 James Darell

130E 8 Carol Ford

131E 1 James Darell

131E 2 André Perlstein

131E 3 Chris Harvey

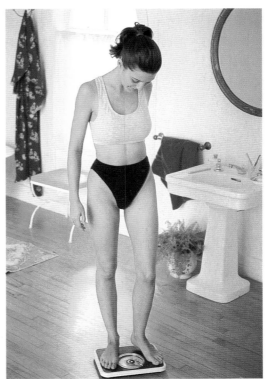

131E 4 David Hanover

131E 5 David Hanover

132E 2 André Perlstein

132E 3 Peter Correz

132E I John Fortunato

132E 4 André Perlstein

132E 5 André Perlstein

132E 6 André Perlstein

132E 7 André Perlstein

132E 9 Rick Rusing

132E 8 André Perlstein

133E 1 Markus Amon

133E 2 André Perlstein

133E 3 Peter Correz

133E 4 Peter Correz

133E 5 James Darell

133E 6 Chris Harvey

133E 7 André Perlstein

133E 8 André Perlstein

133E 9 Jean-François Causse

135E 1 Peter Correz

135E 2 Elan Sun Star

135E 3 Garry Hunter

135E 5 Peter Correz

135E 4 Ken Fisher

136E 1 Dennis O'Clair

136E 2 Chris Harvey

136E 3 Bob Torrez

136E 4 Robert Armstrong

136E 5 Peter Correz

136E 6 Peter Correz

136E 7 Peter Correz

136E 8 Elan Sun Star

137E 1 Ken Fisher

137E 2 Peter Correz

137E 3 Elan Sun Star

137E 5 Chris Harvey

137E 4 Ken Fisher

138E 3 André Perlstein

138E 1 Bob Torrez

138E 2 Dan Bosler

138E 5 André Perlstein

138E 4 Manfred Mehlig

138E 6 Cliff Hollenbeck

138E 7 Peter Correz

138E 8 Peter Correz

138E 9 Ken Fisher

139E 1 Peter Correz

139E 2 Elan Sun Star

139E 3 Peter Correz

139E 4 Peter Correz

139E 5 André Perlstein

139E 6 Elan Sun Star

139E 7 Jean-François Causse

140E 1 Peter Correz

140E 2 Warwick Kent

140E 3 Peter Correz

140E 4 Elan Sun Star

140E 5 Peter Correz

140E 6 Frank Herholdt

140E 7 Peter Correz

140E 8 André Perlstein

141E 1 Darrell Wong

141E 2 Peter Correz

141E 3 Art Brewer

141E 5 André Perlstein

141E 4 Elan Sun Star

142E 3 Elan Sun Star

142E 1 André Perlstein

142E 2 Kurt Coste

142E 6 Peter Correz

142E 4 Peter Correz

142E 5 Ken Fisher

142E 7 Frank Orel

142E 8 Frank Orel

142E 9 Ken Fisher

143E 1 Frank Orel

143E 2 Peter Correz

143E 3 André Perlstein

143E 4 Frank Orel

143E 5 Peter Correz

143E 6 Ken Fisher

143E 7 Philip & Karen Smith

143E 8 Peter Correz

144E 1 Tony Arruza

144E 2 Peter Correz

144E 3 Art Brewer

144E 4 Peter Correz

144E 5 Dave Jacobs

144E 6 Ken Fisher

144E 7 Peter Correz

144E 8 André Perlstein

145E 1 Pascal Crapet

145E 2 Nicholas DeVore

145E 3 Peter Newton

145E 4 Pete Seaward

145E 5 Peter Correz

145E 6 Jean-Marc Truchet

145E 9 Pete Seaward

145E 7 Hugh Sitton

145E 8 Pete Seaward

146E 1 Burma, young Buddhist monks/Nancy Bushnell

147E I New York/Mark Segal

147E 2 New York/Joseph Pobereskin

147E 3 New York, Lincoln Center, Metropolitan Opera/Rohan Van Twest

147E 4 New York/Joseph Pobereskin

147E 5 New York, Empire State and Chrysler Buildings/Jon Ortner

147E 6 New York/Joseph Pobereskin

147E 7 New York/Richard Elliott

147E 9 New York, Upper West Side, Central Park/David Maisel

147E 8 New York/Joseph Pobereskin

148E 1 New York, Twin Towers of World Trade Center/Jon Ortner

148E 2 New York, Lincoln Center/Jon Ortner

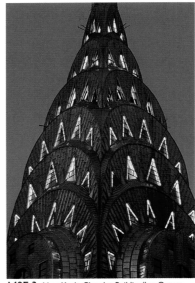

148E 3 New York, Chrysler Building/Jon Ortner

148E 4 New York, Empire State Building/Jon Ortner

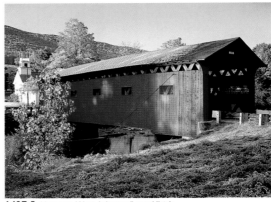

148E 5 Vermont, West Arlington/Larry Ulrich

148E 6 New York, Brooklyn Bridge/Joseph Pobereskin

148E 7 New York/Rohan Van Twest

148E 8 Vermont, Chelsea/Larry Ulrich

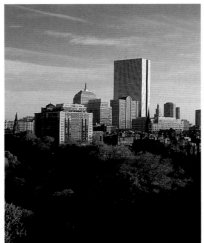

148E 9 Massachusetts, Boston/Chris Cheadle

148E 10 New York/Mark Segal

149E 1 California, Los Angeles/Christopher Bissell

149E 2 Hawaii/Elan Sun Star

149E 3 California, San Francisco, financial district/Robert Shafer

149E 4 California, San Francisco/Chad Ehlers

149E 5 California, San Francisco, Golden Gate Bridge/Donovan Reese

149E 6 Utah, 1949 Buick Roadmaster/Rob Boudreau

149E 7 California, Los Angeles/Ken Biggs

149E 8 California, Los Angeles/Ken Biggs

149E 9 California, San Francisco, Bay Bridge/Cosmo Condina

149E 10 California, Palm Springs, truck stop, replica dinosaur housing souvenir shop/Bob Torrez

150E 1 Nevada, Las Vegas/Mark Segal

150E 2 California, Yosemite National Park/David Hanson

150E 3 Alaska/John Warden

150E 4 Washington, Seattle/Dave Jacobs

150E 5 Washington, Mount Shuksan/Robert Everts

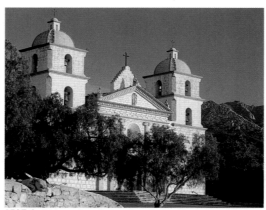

150E 6 California, Santa Barbara, Santa Barbara Mission/Larry Ulrich

150E 7 California/Alan Levenson

150E 8 Washington, Seattle/Karl Weatherly

150E 9 Arizona, Grand Canyon, Colorado River/John Beatty

151E 1 Illinois, Chicago/Mark Segal

151E 2 Donovan Reese

151E 3 Illinois, Chicago/Chris Cheadle

151E 4 Montana, Ute Indian in traditional dance costume/John Running

151E 5 Illinois, Chicago/Mark Segal

151E 6 Arizona, Grand Canyon/Gerard Pile

151E 7 Texas, Dallas, outdoor concert/Keith Wood

151E 8 South Dakota, Mount Rushmore/Glen Allison

151E 9 Utah, Zion National Park/John Warden

151E 10 Arizona, Monument Valley/Rob Boudreau

152E 1   South Dakota, Lakota Indian in traditional costume/Suzanne Murphy

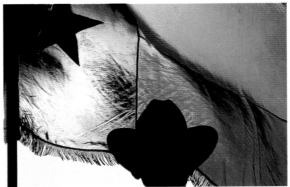

152E 2   Texas/Donovan Reese

152E 3   Washington DC, the Capitol/Doug Armand

152E 4   Arizona, Grand Canyon/Donovan Reese

152E 5   Donovan Reese

152E 6   Washington DC, White House/Paul Kenward

152E 7   Georgia, Atlanta/Jon Riley

152E 8   Georgia, Atlanta/Donovan Reese

152E 10   South Carolina/David Maisel

152E 9   Washington DC, Pennsylvania Avenue, the Capitol/Doug Armand

153E 1 Hawaii, Oahu, Honolulu, Waikiki Beach/Mark Segal

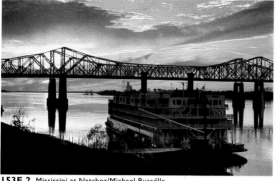

153E 2 Mississipi at Natchez/Michael Bussélle

153E 3 Hawaii, Kauai Island/Kurt Coste

153E 4 Florida, Miami/Cosmo Condina

153E 5 Louisiana, New Orleans/Bob Krist

153E 6 Hawaii/Heather Titus

153E 7 Florida, Orlando, Sea World/Tony Arruza

153E 8 Florida, Miami/Nigel Atherton

153E 9 Hawaii Volcanoes National Park/Brad Lewis

153E 10 Louisiana, New Orleans/David Leach

154E 3 Ontario, Toronto/John Edwards

154E 1 Ontario, Niagara Falls/Doug Armand

154E 2 Ontario, Ottawa, Parliament Hill in distance/Paul Harrison

154E 4 Alberta, Banff National Park/Kenji Ishikura

154E 5 Quebec, Inuit boy/Philippe Cornut

154E 6 British Columbia, Vancouver/Richard Elliott

154E 7 British Columbia, Victoria/Matt Lambert

154E 8 Ontario, Ottawa, Parliament Buildings
Kevin Miller

154E 9 Alberta, Calgary/Glen Allison

154E 10 Alberta, Banff National Park/Nick Geary

155E 1   Ontario, Niagara Falls/Doug Armand

155E 2   Ontario, Toronto/John Edwards

155E 3   Quebec, Montreal/Glen Allison

155E 4   Alberta, Banff National Park/John Edwards

155E 7   Ontario, Toronto/Donald Nausbaum

155E 5   Quebec, Quebec City, Château Frontenac
Glen Allison

155E 6   Hudson Bay, Inuit people/David Hiser

155E 8   British Columbia, Vancouver/Richard Johnston

155E 9   Ontario, Ottawa, Parliament Buildings
in background/John Edwards

155E 10   British Columbia, Kitwanga/John Warden

156E 2 US Virgin Islands, St Thomas, Charlotte Amalie/Cosmo Condina

156E 3 Barbados, Mullins Bay/Doug Armand

156E 1 Netherlands Antilles, Aruba, carnival
Bob Krist

156E 4 St Barthélemy/Steve Murray

156E 5 St Lucia/Robert Everts

156E 6 St Lucia, Soufrière Bay/Doug Armand

156E 7 US Virgin Islands, St Thomas, Charlotte
Amalie/Cosmo Condina

156E 8 St Lucia/Chad Ehlers

156E 9 Bahamas, Exuma Islands, Stocking/Gary Brettnacher

156E 10 Bermuda/Bob Krist

157E 1 St Barthélemy/Mark Lewis

157E 2 Guadeloupe, carnival/Sylvain Grandadam

157E 3 Barbados/Tony Arruza

157E 4 US Virgin Islands, St John, Trunk Bay
Cosmo Condina

157E 5 St Lucia, the Pitons/Bob Krist

157E 6 British Virgin Islands, Tortola/Tom and Michelle Grimm

157E 8 Tobago, Pigeon Point/Pete Seaward

157E 7 St Lucia, Soufrière/Bob Krist

157E 9 Antigua, St John's Harbour/Doug Armand

157E 10 St Barthélemy, Gustavia/Steve Murray

158E 3 Bolivia/Gerard Pile

158E 1 Peru/Jerry Alexander

158E 2 Mexico, folk dancers/Bob Thomason

158E 4 Brazil, Rio de Janeiro/Nigel Snowdon

158E 5 Brazil, rain forest/Donald Nausbaum

158E 6 Peru, Machu Picchu/Michael Scott

158E 7 Mexico, Yucatán, Tulum, El Castillo/Robert Frerck

158E 8 Brazil, Rio de Janeiro, Christ the Redeemer statue/Thierry Cazabon

158E 9 Mexico, Mexico City/Robert Frerck

158E 10 Brazil, Rio de Janeiro, Ipanema Beach/Hiroyuki Yamaguchi

159E 1 Venezuela/Gerard Pile

159E 2 Venezuela, the Amazon, Mejecodoteri
woman/Gerard Pile

159E 3 Brazil, Rio de Janeiro, carnival/Ary Diesendruck

159E 4 Mexico, Yucatán, Sayil, El Palacio/Robert Frerck

159E 5 Guatemala/Pierre Bertillon

159E 6 Mexico, Acapulco/Cosmo Condina

159E 7 Brazil, Rio de Janeiro, carnival/Ary Diesendruck

159E 8 Mexico, Yucatán, Chichén Itzá, Chac Mool Altar and Temple
Robert Frerck

159E 9 Argentina/Brazil border, Iguassú Falls/John Warden

159E 10 Brazil, Rio de Janeiro/Ary Diesendruck

160E 1 London, Tower Bridge/Shaun Egan

160E 2 London, Houses of Parliament/Joe Cornish

160E 3 London/Shaun Egan

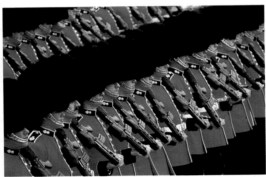

160E 4 London, Trooping the Colour/Ed Pritchard

160E 5 London, Houses of Parliament/Joe Cornish

160E 6 London/Joe Cornish

160E 7 London, Houses of Parliament and Big Ben
Joe Cornish

160E 8 London, Buckingham Palace/Geoff Johnson

160E 9 London, Tower Bridge/Hideo Kurihara

160E 10 London, financial district/Ed Pritchard

161E 1 London, Portobello Road market/Glen Allison

161E 2 London, Grenadier Guards/Glen Allison

161E 3 London, Trafalgar Square/Joe Cornish

161E 4 London, Houses of Parliament/Joe Cornish

161E 5 London, Big Ben/Glen Allison

161E 6 London, Big Ben/Grant Taylor

161E 7 London, St Paul's Cathedral/Shaun Egan

162E 1 Scotland, Edinburgh, Princes Street/Richard Elliott

162E 2 England, Cambridge, River Cam/John Beatty

162E 3 England/Duncan Wherrett

162E 4 England/Julian Calder

162E 5 Scotland, the Highlands/Joe Cornish

162E 6 England, Oxford University/Charlie Waite

162E 7 England, Avon, Bath, Roman Baths
Ed Pritchard

162E 8 England, Wiltshire, Westbury White Horse/John Freeman

162E 9 England, Suffolk, Cavendish/Charlie Waite

162E 10 England/Hilarie Kavanagh

163E 1   Ireland/Joe Cornish

163E 2   England, East Sussex, Bodiam Castle/Patrick Ingrand

163E 3   England, Devon, Dawlish/Peter Cade

163E 4   Ireland, County Cork, Healey Pass/Joe Cornish

163E 5   Ireland, County Mayo, Achill Island/Joe Cornish

163E 6   England, Yorkshire/Rob Talbot

163E 7   England, Kent, Leeds Castle/Patrick Ingrand

163E 8   England, Shropshire/David Paterson

163E 9   England, Cornwall, St Michael's Mount
Charlie Waite

163E 10   Ireland, Dublin/John Bassett

163E 11   England, Dartmoor/Jane Gifford

© TONY STONE IMAGES 1994

164E 1 Steven Rothfeld

164E 2 Paris/Nello Giambi

164E 3 Paris, Galeries Lafayette/Glen Allison

164E 4 Paris, Champs Elysées/Richard Passmore

164E 5 Paris, La Défense, financial district/Pascal Crapet

164E 6 Paris, Pompidou Centre/Suzanne Geary

164E 7 Paris/Jean-Marc Truchet

164E 8 Paris, Nôtre-Dame/Dave Jacobs

164E 9 Paris, La Défense, financial district/Doug Armand

164E 10 Paris, Champs Elysées/Peter Phipp

164E 11 Paris/Carole Elies

165E 1 Paris, Louvre and Pyramid/Doug Armand

165E 2 Paris/Chad Ehlers

165E 3 Paris, Sacré Cœur/Doug Armand

165E 4 Paris, Trocadéro/Sylvain Grandadam

165E 5 Paris, Jardin des Tuileries/Doug Armand

165E 7 Paris, the Arch at La Défense, financial district/Glen Allison

165E 6 Paris/Doug Armand

166E 1 Barry Lewis

166E 2 Patrick Ingrand

166E 3 Normandy, Rouen/Suzanne Geary

166E 4 Côte d'Azur, Menton/Richard Passmore

166E 5 Ile de France, Seine et Marne, Château de Fontainebleau
Pascal Crapet

166E 6 Provence, Bonnieux/Joe Cornish

166E 7 Loire Valley, Château Chenonceau/Patrick Ingrand

166E 8 Bourgogne, vineyards/Maurice Huser

166E 9 Maurice Huser

166E 10 Normandy/Suzanne Geary

167E 1 Loire Valley, Château Chambord/Stephen Studd

167E 2 Brittany/Joe Cornish

167E 3 Normandy, Mont St Michel/Joe Cornish

167E 4 Provence/Joe Cornish

167E 5 Ardèche, Balazuc/Michael Busselle

167E 6 Michael Busselle

167E 7 Côte d'Azur, Nice/Richard Passmore

167E 8 Beaujolais/Steven Rothfeld

167E 9 Richard Passmore

168E 1 Rothenburg/Hideo Kurihara

168E 2 Frankfurt, financial district/Hans Peter Merten

168E 3 Berlin, Kurfürstendamm/John Lamb

168E 4 the Rhine, Boppard/Stephen Studd

168E 5 Esslingen/Chad Ehlers

168E 6 Berlin, Kaiser Wilhelm church/Barry Rowland

168E 7 Berlin, Brandenburg Gate/John Lamb

169E 1 Bavaria/Ralf Schultheiss

169E 2 Berlin, Kaiser Wilhelm church/Doug Armand

169E 3 Bavaria, Munich, Marienplatz/Chad Ehlers

169E 4 Bavaria, Munich, Oktoberfest
Sylvain Grandadam

169E 5 Mosel Valley, Cochem/Stephen Studd

169E 6 Berlin, the Reichstag/Rohan Van Twest

169E 7 Frankfurt, financial district/Ed Pritchard

170E 2 Frankfurt/Stephen Studd

170E 1 Berlin, Charlottenburg Palace/John Lamb

170E 3 Bavaria, Neuschwanstein/Doug Armand

170E 4 Frankfurt, Römerberg Square/Klaus Hackenburg

170E 5 Bavaria, Munich/Ulli Seer

170E 6 Heidelberg, Heidelberg Castle/Stephen Studd

170E 7 Berlin, the Reichstag/John Lamb

170E 8 Cologne/Stephen Studd

171E 1 Switzerland, Lucerne, Chapel Bridge and Water Tower
Shaun Egan

171E 2 Switzerland, Berne, Grindelwald/Shaun Egan

171E 3 Switzerland, Bernese Oberland, Kandersteg/Siegfried Eigstler

171E 4 Austria, Hallstatt/Hans Peter Merten

171E 7 Austria, Tirol, Going/Manfred Mehlig

171E 5 Switzerland, the Matterhorn
Jean-François Causse

171E 6 Switzerland, Geneva, Lake Geneva/Oliver Benn

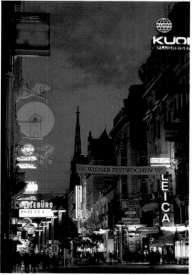
171E 10 Austria, Vienna, Kartnerstrasse
Doug Armand

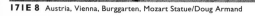
171E 8 Austria, Vienna, Burggarten, Mozart Statue/Doug Armand

171E 9 Switzerland, Bernese Oberland, Gstaad/Siegfried Eigstler

172E 1 Holland, Amsterdam, Amstel canal/Ed Pritchard

172E 2 Belgium, Antwerp, Cathedral of Our Lady
Richard Elliott

172E 3 Holland, Amsterdam, Noordzee canal/Manfred Mehlig

172E 4 Belgium, Brussels,Grand Place/Richard Elliott

172E 5 Holland/Johan Elzenga

172E 6 Norway, Oslo/Richard Elliott

172E 7 Denmark, Copenhagen, Little Mermaid
Tony Craddock

172E 8 Denmark, Copenhagen, Tivoli Gardens, Pimb restaurant
Shaun Egan

172E 9 Denmark, Copenhagen, Nyhavn canal/Hans Peter Merten

172E 10 Belgium, Brussels, EC Headquarters/Hilarie Kavanagh

173E 1 Holland, Alkmaar/Glen Allison

173E 2 Norway, Oslo, Royal Palace/Arnulf Husmo

173E 3 Holland, Amsterdam, Prinsengracht canal/John Lamb

173E 4 Holland, Amsterdam, Leidseplein/Glen Allison

173E 5 Norway, Geirangerfjord/Paul Kenward

173E 6 Norway, Bergen/Bob Krist

173E 7 Belgium, Brussels, Grand Place/Hideo Kurihara

173E 8 Sweden, Kristianstad, Vittskovle and water garden/Chad Ehlers

173E 9 Denmark, Hillerod, Frederiskborg Castle/Gerard Pile

173E 10 Sweden, Stockholm, Saltsjön (estuary to Baltic)/Chad Ehlers

174E 1 Venice, carnival/Jamey Stillings

174E 2 Venice/John McDermott

174E 3 Rome, St Peter's Square, Carabinieri
Stephen Studd

174E 4 Rome, Piazza Navona, Neptune Fountain
Stephen Studd

174E 5 Rome, Roman Forum/Stephen Studd

174E 6 Venice, Santa Maria della Salute/John Lamb

174E 7 Poggio, Elba/Charlie Waite

174E 8 Rome, Church of Santa Maria in Cosmedin,
Mouth of Truth/Stephen Studd

174E 9 Florence, Ponte Vecchio/Richard Elliott

174E 10 Venice, Grand Canal/Jamey Stillings

175E 1 Florence, Duomo/Trevor Wood

175E 2 Milan, Duomo/Simeone Huber

175E 3 Leaning Tower of Pisa/Tony Craddock

175E 4 Tuscany/Trevor Wood

175E 6 Rome, Trevi Fountain, Palazzo Poli
Glen Allison

175E 5 Venice, San Giorgio Maggiore/John Lamb

175E 8 Rome, the Colosseum/Stephen Studd

175E 7 Venice/Jamey Stillings

176E 1 Rome, Piazza Navona, Neptune Fountain/Stephen Studd

176E 2 Milan, Duomo/Ken Whitmore

176E 3 Rome, Colosseum/Stephen Studd

176E 4 Venice, Grand Canal, Santa Maria della Salute/Jamey Stillings

176E 5 Rome, St Peter's Basilica, the Pope holding mass/Sylvain Grandadam

176E 6 Venice/Gerard Pile

176E 7 Liguria, Camogli/John McDermott

176E 8 Rome, Ponte Sant'Angelo, River Tiber/Stephen Studd

176E 10 Tuscany, San Gimignano/Joe Cornish

176E 9 Venice, San Giorgio Maggiore church/John Lamb

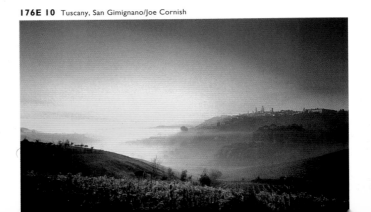

177E 1 Turkey, Istanbul, Blue Mosque/Hugh Sitton

177E 2 Greece, Mykonos/Sylvain Grandadam

177E 5 Turkey/David Hanson

177E 3 Turkey, Pamukkale, travertine pools
Gerard Pile

177E 4 Turkey, Ephesus, Library of Celsus/Nigel Hillier

177E 6 Turkey, Olu Deniz/Richard Passmore

177E 7 Turkey, Istanbul, Aya Sophia/Hugh Sitton

177E 8 Greece, Santorini/Hugh Sitton

177E 9 Greece, Rhodes, Lindos/Hideo Kurihara

177E 10 Greece, Athens, the Temple of Olympian Zeus/John Lamb

177E 11 Greece, Athens, Acropolis/John Lamb

178E 2 Spain, Andalusia, Ronda, Guadalevin Gorge and Tajo Bridge
Shaun Egan

178E 1 Portugal/David Hanson

178E 3 Portugal, Albufeira/David Hanson

178E 4 Spain, Andalusia, almond groves/Dave Jacobs

178E 5 Spain/Joe Cornish

178E 6 Spain, Barcelona, La Pedrera (designed by Gaudi)/Frank Orel

178E 7 Spain, Barcelona, Sagrada Familia/Doug Armand

178E 8 Tenerife, Caldera de Las Canadas, Los Roques/Hugh Sitton

178E 9 Malta, Marsamxett Harbour/Hideo Kurihara

178E 10 Spain, Madrid, Plaza de la Cibeles
Doug Armand

179E 1 Spain, Old Castile, Segovia, the Alcázar/Joe Cornish

179E 2 Portugal, Oporto/Manfred Mehlig

179E 5 Spain, Barcelona/Doug Armand

179E 3 Spain, Mallorca, Porto Colom
David Tomlinson

179E 4 Spain, Andalusia, Gaucin/Shaun Egan

179E 6 Ibiza, Cala Bassa/Manfred Mehlig

179E 7 Portugal/Rhonda Klevansky

179E 8 Portugal, Algarve, Praia de Anna
David Hanson

179E 9 Portugal, Lisbon, Discoverers' Monument/Ed Pritchard

179E 10 Spain, Madrid, Plaza de Espâna, Cervantes Monument
Hideo Kurihara

180E 3 Russia, Crimea, Yalta, Swallow's Nest Castle
Wolfgang Krammisch

180E 1 Russia, Moscow, St Basil's Cathedral, Monument to
Minin and Pozharsky/Gary Brettnacher

180E 2 Russia, Moscow, GUM department store/John Freeman

180E 4 Czech Republic, Prague, Vltava river/Joe Cornish

180E 5 Poland, Warsaw, Old Market Square/Zygmunt Nowak-Soliński

180E 6 Hungary, Budapest, Castle Palace of Buda/Hideo Kurihara

180E 7 Czech Republic, Prague, St Nicholas Church
Oldrich Karasek

180E 8 Czech Republic, Prague, Smetana Museum
Oldrich Karasek

180E 9 Hungary, Budapest, Chain Bridge

181E 1 Czech Republic, Prague, Charles Bridge/Joe Cornish

181E 3 Czech Republic, Prague, Charles Bridge/Chad Ehlers

181E 2 Russia, Moscow, St Basil's Cathedral
David Sutherland

181E 4 Russia, Pushkin (near St Petersburg),
Catherine's Palace/Sylvain Grandadam

181E 5 Russia, St Petersburg, Winter Palace/Ed Pritchard

181E 6 Czech Republic, Prague, Old Town Hall,
Astronomical Clock/Joe Cornish

181E 8 Russia, Moscow, St Basil's Cathedral/David Sutherland

181E 7 Czech Republic, Prague, Vltava river/Chad Ehlers

182E 1　Morocco, Marrakesh, Djemaa el Fna Square/Rohan Van Twest

182E 2　Algeria, Ghardaia/Warren Jacobs

182E 3　Morocco/Sylvain Grandadam

182E 4　Israel, Jerusalem, Western Wall/Oliver Benn

182E 5　Morocco, Sahara Desert, Berber tribe/Penny Tweedie

182E 6　Israel, Jerusalem/Lucia Pirelli

182E 7　Israel, Jerusalem, Damascus Gate/Oliver Benn

182E 8　Morocco, Berber shepherd/Gerard Del Vecchio

182E 9　Morocco, Berber woman/John Beatty

182E 10　Saudi Arabia, Mecca/Nabeel Turner

183E 1 Luxor, Temple of Karnak/Hugh Sitton

183E 2 Abu Simbel, Temple of Hathor/Stephen Studd

183E 3 the Pyramids of Giza/Hugh Sitton

183E 4 the Pyramids of Giza/David Sutherland

183E 5 Aswan/Hugh Sitton

183E 6 Luxor, Temple of Karnak/Hugh Sitton

183E 7 Luxor, Temple of Karnak, Avenue of Sphinxes/Stephen Studd

183E 8 the Pyramids of Giza/Herb Schmitz

183E 9 the Pyramids of Giza/Hugh Sitton

183E 10 Cairo, Sultan Hasan Mosque/Nabeel Turner

184E 1 Zimbabwe/Ian Murphy

184E 2 Kenya, Masai Mara National Park/Paul Kenward

184E 3 Zimbabwe, Victoria Falls/Ian Murphy

184E 4 Zimbabwe/Ian Murphy

184E 5 Burundi, Ninga drummers/Bruno de Hogues

184E 6 Zambia/Ian Murphy

184E 7 Mozambique/Penny Tweedie

184E 8 lion/Mitch Reardon

184E 9 Tanzania, Serengeti Plain, Ngorongoro Crater behind
Nicholas Parfitt

184E 10 Chad, Kanem, Fulani woman making
butter/Jacques Langoux

185E 1 India/Nicholas DeVore

185E 2 India, Rajasthan, Jaipur, Palace of the Winds/Michael Busselle

185E 3 Burma, woman at prayer/Gerry Soifer

185E 4 India, Taj Mahal/Hilarie Kavanagh

185E 5 Nepal, Kathmandu, Bodhnath stupa
Mike McQueen

185E 6 Burma, Pagan/Nancy Bushnell

185E 7 Burma, young Buddhist monks/Gerry Soifer

185E 8 India, Rajasthan, Udaipur, Lake Palace Hotel/Nicholas DeVore

185E 9 India, Pune/Ben Edwards

186E 2 India, Kashmir, Dal Lake/Margaret Gowan

186E 1 India, Rajasthan, Pushkar/Michael Busselle

186E 3 Sri Lanka/Donald Nausbaum

186E 4 Sri Lanka, Anuradhapura, Thuparama Dagoba
Hugh Sitton

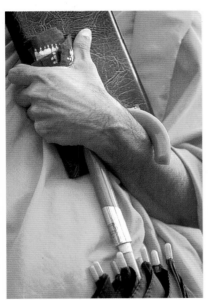

186E 5 Sri Lanka, Buddhist monk/Hugh Sitton

186E 6 Nepal, Sherpa family/Nicholas DeVore

186E 7 Nepal, north-east region/Mike McQueen

186E 8 Sri Lanka, tea picking/Hugh Sitton

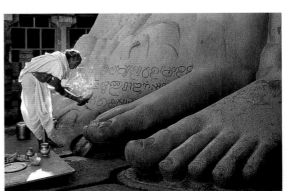

186E 9 India, Taj Mahal/Suzanne Geary

186E 10 India, Sravanabelagola, statue of Gomateshvara/Nicholas DeVore

187E 1 Phuket, Wat Chalong/Hugh Sitton

187E 4 Phuket, Wat Chalong/Hugh Sitton

187E 2 Lamphun, Wat Phra That Hariphunchai/Hugh Sitton

187E 3 Bangkok, Wat Indraviharn/Paul Chesley

187E 5 Buddhist monastery classroom/Paul Chesley

187E 6 Bangkok, Grand Palace/Hugh Sitton

187E 9 Krabi/Hugh Sitton

187E 7 Krabi, Phi Phi Don, overlooking Lohdalum and Pon Sai Bays
Hugh Sitton

187E 8 Chiang Mai, Wat Chiang Man/Hugh Sitton

188E 1 Singapore/Bob Krist

188E 2 Hong Kong/John Callahan

188E 3 Singapore/Hugh Sitton

188E 4 Singapore, Raffles Hotel/Hugh Sitton

188E 5 Hong Kong, Mong Kok/Neil Beer

188E 6 Singapore, financial district/Hugh Sitton

188E 7 Hong Kong, New Territories, Hakka woman/Bryn Campbell

188E 8 Hong Kong, financial district/Neil Beer

188E 9 Hong Kong/John Lamb

188E 10 Singapore, Bugis Street/Bob Krist

189E 1   Malaysia, Penang, Kek Lok Si Temple/Hugh Sitton

189E 4   Malaysia, Penang, Kek Lok Si Temple
Hugh Sitton

189E 2   Vietnam, Ho Chi Minh City, shanty town/Paul Chesley

189E 3   China/Dennis Cox

189E 7   Vietnam, Ho Chi Minh City/Paul Chesley

189E 5   Taiwan, Taipei, Chiang Kai-Shek Memorial
Jerry Lee

189E 6   China, Shanghai, Children's Palace, calligraphy
class/Dennis Cox

189E 10   China, Shanghai/Herb Schmitz

189E 8   China, Great Wall, soldiers/Alain Le Garsmeur

189E 9   Malaysia, Kuala Lumpur, Sultan Abdul Samad
Building/Hugh Sitton

© TONY STONE IMAGES 1994

190E 1 Korea, Seoul, textile shop/Paul Chesley

190E 2 Japan, Mount Fuji/Shizuo Iijima

190E 3 Japan, Tokyo, Shinjuku financial district/Richard Passmore

190E 4 Japan, Kyoto, Shogoin Temple Shinto priest, Nicholas DeVore

190E 5 Japan, Tokyo, family at home/Paul Chesley

190E 6 Japan, Tokyo, Ginza/Keiichi Hirayama

190E 7 Korea, Seoul/Miwako Ikeda

190E 8 Japan, Tokyo/Paul Chesley

191E 1 Mount Fuji, bullet train/Hiroshi Wada

191E 2 Kyoto, geisha/Paul Chesley

191E 3 Kyushu, Beppu, hot springs bath/Paul Chesley

191E 4 Kyoto, Miyako-odari (traditional dance)/Nicholas DeVore

191E 5 sumo wrestling/Chris Cole

191E 7 Tokyo/Jose Raga

191E 6 Kyoto, children fastening Japanese fortunes outside Buddhist temple/Sylvain Grandadam

192E 2 Micronesia, Palau, Kayangel Island/Paul Chesley

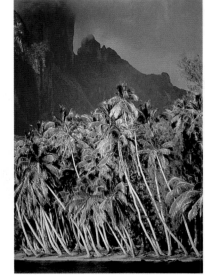

192E 3 French Polynesia, Bora Bora/Paul Berger

192E 1 Bali, rice harvesting/Steve Murray

192E 5 Western Samoa, Savaii Island/David Hiser

192E 4 Bali/Paul Chesley

192E 6 Cook Island/Suzanne Murphy

192E 7 French Polynesia, Bora Bora/Nicholas DeVore

192E 8 Philippines/Paul Chesley

192E 9 Bali/Hilarie Kavanagh

193E 1 Fiji, Turtle Island/David Hiser

193E 2 Bali/Paul Chesley

193E 3 Papua New Guinea/Darryl Torckler

193E 4 Indonesia, Lombok, Gili Air Island/Peter Cade

193E 5 Bali, Buddhist temple stone guard
Paul Chesley

193E 7 Bali/Michael Busselle

193E 6 Indonesia, Jakarta/Paul Chesley

193E 8 Indonesia, Java, Borobudur ruins, Buddha/Paul Chesley

193E 9 Bali, rice terraces/Steve Murray

194E 2 New Zealand, Queenstown/Warren Jacobs

194E 1 Australia, Queensland, Whitsunday Islands/Paul Chesley

194E 4 Australia, Melbourne, skyline from Shrine of Remembrance/Trevor Mein

194E 3 New Zealand, South Island, Southern Alps/Paul Chesley

194E 6 Australia, Uluru National Park, the Olgas/Mitch Reardon

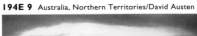

194E 9 Australia, Northern Territories/David Austen

194E 5 New Zealand, North Island, Mount Ngauruhoe/Hideo Kurihara

194E 7 Australia, Aborigine child/Penny Tweedie

194E 8 Australia, Queensland, Surfers Paradise/Zigy Kaluzny

195E I   Australia, Aboriginal bark painting/Penny Tweedie

195E 2   Australia, koala bear/Penny Tweedie

195E 3   Australia, Aborigines/Penny Tweedie

195E 4   Australia, Sydney/Robert Mort

195E 5   Australia, Queensland, Great Barrier
Reef/Paul Chesley

195E 6   New Zealand, Taranaki, Mount Egmont/Oliver Strewe

195E 7   Australia, Sydney/Robin Smith

195E 8   New Zealand, South Island, vineyards/Patrick Eagar

195E 9   Australia, Ayers Rock/Hilarie Kavanagh

Darryl Torckler

197E 1 Yoshihito Manazu

197E 2 Chad Ehlers

197E 3 Tim Brown

197E 4 Ed Pritchard

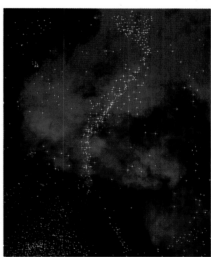

197E 5 Tim Brown

197E 6 Doug Armand

197E 7 Trevor Mein

197E 8

198E 3 Ed Pritchard

198E 2 Fred George

198E 1 David Bassett

198E 4 Stephen Johnson

198E 5 Alastair Laidlaw

198E 6 Shaun Egan

198E 7 Arnulf Husmo

198E 8 David Bassett

198E 9 Kevin Beebe

199E 2 Steve Taylor

199E 1 Steve Taylor

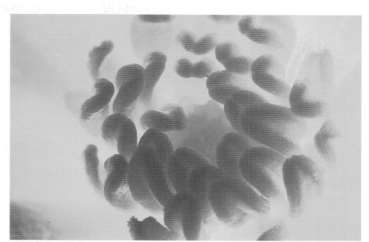

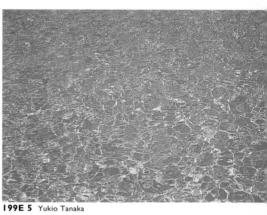

199E 5 Yukio Tanaka

199E 3 Michael Busselle

199E 4 Steve Taylor

199E 8 Dennis O'Clair

199E 6 David Rigg

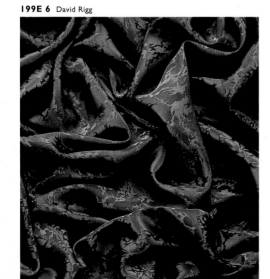

199E 7 Mel Lindstrom

200E 2 Darryl Torckler

200E 1 Larry Ulrich

200E 3 Austin Brown

200E 4 Darryl Torckler

200E 5 Dennis McColeman

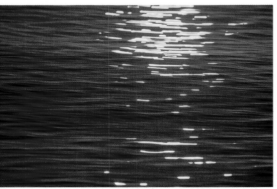

200E 6 John Callahan

200E 7 Peter Cade

200E 8 Mamoru Muto

201E 1 Arnulf Husmo

201E 2 Mark Wagner

201E 3 Jean-Marc Truchet

201E 4 Neil Farrin

201E 5 Arnulf Husmo

201E 6 Darryl Torckler

202E 1 Stephen Studd

202E 2 Ulli Seer

202E 3 Jeremy Walker

202E 4 Magnus Rew

202E 5 Graeme Norways

202E 6 Lorentz Gullachsen

202E 7 Mark Lewis

202E 8 Arnulf Husmo

203E 1 Darryl Torckler

203E 3 Trevor Mein

203E 2 Darryl Torckler

203E 4 John Turner

203E 5 John Warden

203E 6 Paul Berger

204E 2 Graeme Norways

204E 1 Jeremy Walker

204E 4 David Woodfall

204E 3 Arnulf Husmo

204E 5 Austin Brown

204E 6 David Muscroft

204E 7 Darryl Torckler

204E 8 Tony Craddock

204E 9 Martin Barraud

204E 10 Doug Armand

205E 1 Darryl Torckler

205E 2 Darryl Torckler

205E 3 Stephen Studd

205E 4 Pierre Bertillon

205E 5 Darryl Torckler

205E 6 Trevor Mein

205E 7 Pete Seaward

205E 8 Lorentz Gullachsen

205E 9 Colin Raw

206E 1 Magnus Rew

206E 2 David Sutherland

206E 3 Doug Armand

206E 4 Hans Peter Merten

206E 5 Darryl Torckler

206E 6 Donald Nausbaum

206E 7 Arnulf Husmo

206E 8 Tim Brown

207E 1 John Beatty

207E 2 David Hiser

207E 3 Trevor Mein

207E 4 Ralph Wetmore

207E 5 Ralph Wetmore

207E 6 Ralph Wetmore

207E 8 Trevor Mein

207E 7 Rosemary Calvert

208E 1 Peter Cade

208E 2 Paul Berger

208E 3 Dave Bjorn

208E 4 Dave Bjorn

208E 6 Hiroshi Sato

208E 5 Kristian Hilsen

209E 1 Paul Berger

209E 2 Paul Berger

209E 3

209E 4 Neal Mishler

209E 5 Denjiro Sato

209E 6 Darryl Torckler

210E 1 Hugh Sitton

210E 2 Barry Rowland

210E 3 Donovan Reese

210E 4 Sally Mayman

210E 5 Brad Lewis

210E 6 Donovan Reese

210E 7 Joe Cornish

210E 8 Darryl Torckler

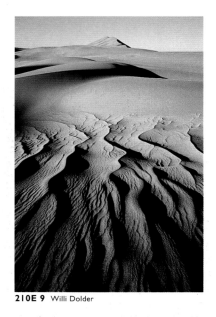
210E 9 Willi Dolder

210E 10 Sally Mayman

211E 1 Richard Johnston

211E 2 Sally Mayman

211E 3 Nicholas DeVore

211E 4 Kristian Hilsen

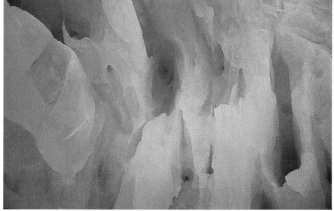

211E 5 John Beatty

211E 6 John Beatty

211E 8 Terje Pettersen

211E 7 Bert Hilger

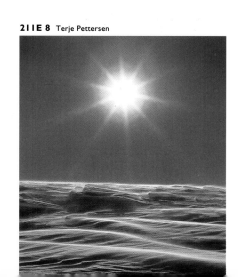

211E 9 Siegfried Eigstler

212E 2 David Woodfall

212E 1 Michael Busselle

212E 3 Michael Busselle

212E 4 Glen Allison

212E 5 Ernst Ziesmann

212E 6 Michael Busselle

212E 8 Steve Murray

212E 7 Richard Johnston

213E 1 Alan Levenson

213E 2 Michael Busselle

213E 3 Dave Jacobs

213E 5 Yoshihiro Takada

213E 6 Iwao Watanabe

213E 4 David Woodfall

213E 7 Michael Busselle

213E 8 James Balog

215E 1 domestic waste dump/Hans Peter Merten

215E 2 stricken oil supertanker Amoco Cadiz/Martin Rogers

215E 3 New Mexico, copper mine/Lester Lefkowitz

215E 4 Poland, acid rain-damaged spruce forest/David Woodfall

215E 6 shag killed by oil pollution/David Woodfall

215E 5 Brazil, rain forest destruction/Jacques Jangoux

216E 1 testing soil for pollutants/Phil Degginger

216E 2 polar bears scavenging in domestic waste dump/David Hiser

216E 3 shag killed by oil pollution/David Woodfall

216E 4 Brazil, rain forest clearance for oil exploration/Sue Cunningham

216E 5 industrial waste treatment/Maurice Huser

216E 6 river polluted with chemical waste/David Woodfall

216E 7 USA, Los Angeles, traffic pollution and congestion/Ken Biggs

216E 8 oil-polluted sea/David Woodfall

216E 9 forest fire/David Frazier

216E 10 acid drainage holding pond, next to iron mine/Thomas Braise

217E 1 wind-powered electricity generators/Glen Allison

217E 2 Malawi, Kapezi refugee camp water well/Penny Tweedie

217E 3 David Maisel

217E 4 Lori Adamski Peek

217E 5 compressed tin cans for recycling
Bruce Hands

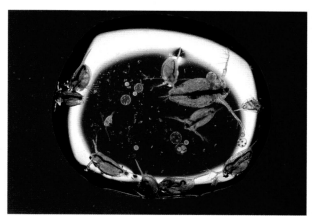

217E 6 microscopic pond life/Spike Walker

217E 8 New Zealand, temperate rain forest
Robert Frerck

217E 7 Stephen Studd

218E 1 Richard Johnston

218E 2 Charles Thatcher

218E 3 John Beatty

218E 4 replanting in forest clearing/Bruce Hands

218E 5 plastic recycling centre/Jon Riley

218E 6 Simon Jauncey

218E 7 Richard Johnston

218E 8 fern growing in volcanic landscape/Darryl Torckler

218E 9 Brazil, rain forest/Jacques Jangoux

219E 1 Red Delicious apples/Bruce Hands

219E 2 Vietnamese pot-bellied pig/Sean Arbabi

219E 3 tilling soil in maize field/Mitch Kezar

219E 5 France, Champagne, vineyards/Fernand Ivaldi

219E 4 rape seed harvesting/Jamey Stillings

220E 1 Glen Allison

220E 2 maize/Andrew Sacks

220E 3 barley field/Stephen Studd

220E 4 wheat/Andrew Sacks

220E 5 rape field/David Woodfall

220E 6 Andrew Sacks

220E 7 Andrew Sacks

220E 8 merlot grapes/Jerry Alexander

221E 1 loading harvested grain onto truck/Jamey Stillings

221E 2 tree growth monitoring/Bob Krist

221E 3 wheat field/Gunter Köhler

221E 4 soya bean seedling/Andrew Sacks

221E 5 harvested field of wheat/Hugh Sitton

221E 7 spraying cotton crop with pesticide/Andrew Sacks

221E 6 alfalfa harvesting/Andrew Sacks

222E 1 spraying orchard with pesticide/Bruce Hands

222E 2 soya bean seedling/Andrew Sacks

222E 3 barley crop monitoring/Richard Surman

222E 4 wheat harvesting/Andrew Sacks

222E 5 Colin Prior

222E 6 barley field/Andrew Sacks

222E 7 grape harvesting/Michael Busselle

222E 8 David Paterson

223E 1 Limousin cow/David Woodfall

223E 2 Ian Shaw

223E 3 yew tree seedlings for use in cancer research
Bruce Hands

223E 4 drying field of cut hay/Bruce Hands

223E 5 straw bales/Charlie Waite

223E 6 Simon Jauncey

223E 7 Tamworth boar/Ben Osborne

224E 2 Alastair Laidlaw

224E 1 Tif Hunter

224E 4 herbs and spices/Charles Thatcher

224E 3 Linda Burgess

224E 7 Malaysian dishes/Trevor Wood

224E 5 Ian O'Leary

224E 6 Thomas Brase

225E 1 Aaron Jones, Aaron Jones Studios

225E 2 Carol Ford

225E 3 Alastair Laidlaw

225E 4 Charles Thatcher

225E 5 Linda Burgess

225E 6 Thomas Braise

225E 7 Aaron Jones, Aaron Jones Studios

227E 1 Bengal tiger/James Balog

227E 3 Hamadryas baboon/Bill Ivy

227E 2 rhinoceros/Ian Murphy

227E 4 hippopotamus/Ian Murphy

227E 5 ostrich family/Paul Kenward

228E 1 lion cubs/Johan Elzenga

228E 2 African elephant/Mitch Reardon

228E 3 Cape buffaloes/Nicholas DeVore

228E 4 lioness/Peter Lamberti

228E 5 jaguar/James Balog

228E 6 African elephant and calf/Mitch Reardon

228E 7 cheetah/Peter Lamberti

228E 8 lion/Mitch Reardon

228E 9 lowland gorilla/James Balog

229E 1 giraffe/Penny Tweedie

229E 2 Bengal tiger (endangered variety with Siberian tiger ancestry)/James Balog

229E 3 African elephant calf/Jeanne Drake

229E 4 young impalas/Nicholas Parfitt

229E 5 leopard/Jeanne Drake

229E 6 zebras/Gary Owen

229E 7 hippopotamus/Peter Lamberti

229E 8 young baboons/Jeanne Drake

229E 9 lioness/Mitch Reardon

230E 1 bald eagle/John Warden

230E 2 brown bear/David Myers

230E 3 Unita ground squirrel/Tom Tietz

230E 4 racoon/Tom Tietz

230E 5 bison/Rod Planck

230E 6 brown bear/James Balog

230E 7 elk/Gary Brettnacher

231E 1 pica (alpine rodent)/Tom Tietz

231E 4 brown bear/John Warden

231E 3 bald eagle/Tim Flach

231E 2 black-tailed prairie hare/Tom Tietz

231E 7 Canadian lynx/Tom Tietz

231E 5 northern flicker bird/Mervyn Rees

231E 6 mountain lion/Tom Tietz

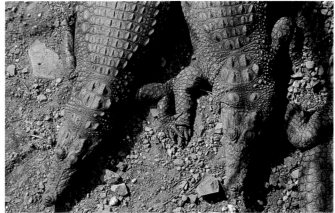

232E 1 crocodiles/Ian Murphy

232E 2 Red Sea, rathbournes sweepers/Marc Chamberlain

232E 3 South Pacific, school of Koheru fish/Darryl Torckler

232E 4 bullfrog/Bill Ivy

232E 5 European swallowtail butterfly/Mervyn Rees

232E 6 yellow-headed collared lizard/Rod Planck

232E 7 Indonesia, Celebes Sea, school of jacks/Norbert Wu

232E 8 dolphins/Bill Pogue

232E 9 Galapagos shark/Darryl Torckler

233E 1 Pacific Ocean, sea turtle/Kevin Sweeney

233E 2 crocodile/Mitch Reardon

233E 3 Red Sea, lyre-tailed goldfish/Marc Chamberlain

233E 4 jumping spider/Steve Taylor

233E 5 Pacific Ocean, clown fish in sea anemone/Marc Chamberlain

233E 6 leaf cutter ants/Gay Bumgarner

233E 7 ladybird/John Beatty

234E 1 polar bears/David Myers

234E 2 great grey owl/Rod Planck

234E 5 polar bear/David Myers

234E 3 red squirrel/David Hosking

234E 4 whitetail deer/Jeanne Drake

234E 6 red fox/Tom Ulrich

234E 7 grey wolf/Tom Tietz

234E 8 sea otter/Norbert Wu

234E 9 King penguins/David Myers

234E 10 Gentoo penguins/Martin Rogers

235E 1 horses/Peter Pearson

235E 2 dog/Chip Henderson

235E 3 redwing blackbird chick/Bill Ivy

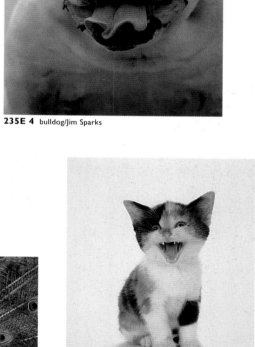

235E 4 bulldog/Jim Sparks

235E 5 young great-horned owl/Tom Tietz

235E 6 peacock/Tony Craddock

235E 7 kitten/Robert Haddock

235E 8 horses/Hideo Kurihara

235E 9 desert tortoise/Mark Lewis

James Balog's career as a photographer and artist evolved from his lifelong passion about the relationship between mankind and the natural world. James travelled the world to capture images of endangered and protected species, the subject of his award-winning book *Survivors,* published in 1990. While working on *Survivors,* he was exceptionally moved by his experience with Great apes and began to develop the concept which you see in the following pages – wonderful images from his latest book, *Anima.* The images in this portfolio explore the link between humans and chimpanzees. James staged them artfully with the intention of making us question our assumptions about ourselves and our place in the world. "The chimpanzee is humanity's nearest genetic relative, our genes are 98.4% identical," says the Colorado-based photographer. "Chimps experience joy, sorrow, fear, pleasure and love – just like humans. So they become a perfect vehicle through which to challenge our own cultural beliefs." James Balog's photographs and photo-essays have appeared in *National Geographic, Life, Geo* and many other publications, and his work has been widely exhibited in Europe and North America, earning him the status of one of the world's great contemporary photographers.

239E I

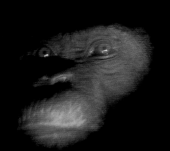

240E 2